THE MERCIFUL GOAL

"I am neither a holy man nor a superman, but one who has learned simple techniques for circumventing pain

"Just as I learned to master pain so that I can walk unharmed through hot coals or lie unmarked on beds of nails, so can you learn to control the pain of backache, arthritis, headache, or any other affliction that might decrease your full enjoyment of life.

"I believe that the step-by-step method toward self-mastery can give anyone complete control over himself or herself . . . once one gains such mind and body control, it is not difficult to eliminate a particular pain, ache, discomfort, tension, or ailment."

—KOMAR

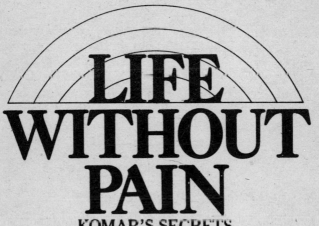

LIFE WITHOUT PAIN

KOMAR'S SECRETS OF PAIN CONTROL

KOMAR
WITH BRAD STEIGER

BERKLEY BOOKS, NEW YORK

LIFE WITHOUT PAIN

A Berkley Book / published by arrangement with
the author

PRINTING HISTORY
Berkley edition / May 1979
Second printing / September 1982

ISBN: 0-425-05709-7

A BERKLEY BOOK ® TM 757,375
The name "BERKLEY" and the stylized "B" with design
are trademarks belonging to Berkley Publishing Corporation.
PRINTED IN THE UNITED STATES OF AMERICA

Contents

Foreword

No book can do justice to an individual as unique as
Komar; in fact, even a movie would have difficulty
catching the drama that he portrays.

I was first introduced to Komar about four years
ago. He came up to be evaluated as an individual who
performs uniquely painful-looking tasks. We had the
scientific and personal pleasure of seeing Komar
withstand needles through the arm, hands in a bucket
of ice water, and lying on a bed of nails with two people
jumping up and down on his chest while we recorded
EKG, EEG, respiration, galvanic skin response, etc.
To all of these potentially destructive procedures,

Komar smiled, produced a little increase in alpha wave activity, and nothing else. I should note that I was able to do all of these things myself through having practiced voluntary self-regulatory techniques for some time when I first met Komar, with the exception of having two people jump up and down on my chest! Although I had no qualms at all about lying on the bed of nails, I definitely am not ready to have 350 pounds of weight bobbing up and down on my chest while I'm doing it.

Even more dramatically, on my wife's birthday in 1977, Komar performed a feat which I had heard about a number of times but could never quite understand as possible until I saw him do it: I built a fire, the flames of which leaped over twenty feet into the air when it was burning. When it had burned to a red-hot-coal stage, five to six inches in depth, approximately twenty feet long and four feet wide, I took a six-foot rake at arm's length to level the coals so that there were no large irregularities in the bed. My eyebrows were singed at about a seven-foot distance from the coals. When the time arrived for his display, Komar then walked around the bed of coals several times, smoking a cigarette and drinking a Coke. Suddenly he tossed the can to one side, threw the cigarette into the coals, and, without hesitating, walked at an ordinary pace across the bed of coals. I immediately examined his feet when he arrived at the other side of the coals. They were cool, soft as a baby's feet, and undamaged. The temperature of the coals measured 1,375 degrees Fahrenheit.

We scientists can observe activities such as this, but we cannot explain them. The best we can do is say that our knowledge and understanding of the capabilities of the mind and unconsciousness are indeed limited—

well below that which can be and has been accomplished.

       —C. Norman Shealy, M.D., Ph.D., Director
         The Pain & Health Rehabilitation Center
         La Crosse, Wisconsin

INTRODUCTION:

THE REMARKABLE KOMAR

by Brad Steiger

A hush fell over the guests at the Wayne County Home's annual chicken barbecue. An imposing figure clad in blue pantaloons, gold shirt, and white turban had replaced the master of ceremonies at the microphone. Komar the Hindu Fakir was about to speak.

"Ladies and gentlemen," Komar began, "if everyone will follow me to the barbecue pit, I will attempt to walk barefoot across the hot coals!"

Approximately a thousand people accepted Komar's invitation. When they arrived at the barbecue pit, they saw a bed of hot coals, the aftermath of twenty-foot flames which had risen to such a height at one time during the evening that they had threatened to spread to nearby trees. The spectators could come no closer than fifteen feet—the heat was that intense!

Komar gazed into the pit. His features were calm.

He waited while two men with rakes spread the coals until the bed was twenty-five feet long and six inches deep. The raking process exposed more of the coals to the open air, and they changed color from orange to angry red.

As Komar removed his sandals, some of the spectators tried to move in closer, but once again they were turned back by the heat.

Komar looked directly into the coals, then thrust in one foot.

Some of the spectators turned their faces away as the Hindu fakir pulled up the legs of his pantaloons and stepped upon the coals.

He took one step, then another, then leisurely began his walk toward the other end of the pit.

In the audience, a woman tugged at her husband's sleeve. "Look!" she gasped. "His pants legs are melting!"

Komar seemed not to notice. With each step, the coals snapped and spat, as though in protest. Finally he reached the other side where a doctor waited.

"Let me help you," offered the doctor, extending his hand.

"No, thank you," replied Komar, "I'm all right."

The doctor conducted an on-the-spot examination, then confirmed the fakir's self-diagnosis. Except for a tiny tinge of red, Komar's feet showed no sign of their fiery ordeal!

Unable to believe his own findings, the doctor took

a second look. "Not even a small blister," he announced to the spectators.

Firewalking is a phenomenon that remains a mystery even to those who have spent years researching the subject; but to the uninitiated, as well as the experienced investigator, any one of Komar's pain-control demonstrations boggles the mind!

He lies on a bed of sharpened nails while a husky member of the audience crushes a chunk of cement on his body with a sledgehammer.

He stretches serenely on his nailbed while heavy men from the audience stand on a board placed across his chest.

He leaps from a raised platform onto a bed of nails with his bare feet.

He pushes a nail through a one-inch board, his hand protected only by a handkerchief.

He bends bars with his bare hands.

Komar is listed in the 1976 edition of the famous *Guinness Book of World Records* as holding the record for the hottest firewalk. According to the book's editors: "The highest temperature endured in a firewalk is 1,220°F. for 25 feet by 'Komar' of Wooster, Ohio, at the Phoenix Psychic Seminar, Arizona, on March 7, 1975. The temperature was measured by a pyrometer." Awaiting recognition from the *Guinness* editors is an incredible 1,494-degree firewalk set at Maidenhead, England, in July of 1976.

The *Guinness Book of World Records* credits Komar with two additional international record feats: "The duration record for non-stop lying on a bed of nails [needle-sharp 6-inch nails, 2 inches apart] is 25 hours 20 minutes by [Komar] at Wooster, Ohio, July 22–23, 1971. The greatest live weight borne on a bed of

nails is also held by Komar with 4 persons aggregating
1,142 lbs., standing on him on the Mike Douglas Show
on TV in Philadelphia on March 26, 1974." Komar
recently performed this feat in Chicago while sandwiched between two beds of nails and supporting an
aggregate 1,642 lbs.

On July 17, 1973, medical tests were conducted at
the Pain Rehabilitation Center, a unit of St. Francis's
Hospital in LaCrosse, Wisconsin, by Dr. C. Norman
Shealy, recognized as one of the most knowledgeable
authorities on pain in the United States. The subject of
the tests was Vernon E. Craig—better known as
Komar, the Hindu Fakir. The objective of the tests at
the Pain Rehabilitation Center was to find out how
Komar is able to control pain, to seemingly fly away
from intense physical discomfort.

Dr. Shealy was willing to undertake the tests
because he is interested in any technique that may offer
aid in the alleviation of pain. As a neurosurgeon, Dr.
Shealy has a thorough knowledge of the relationships
of pain to the nervous system and the brain. Dr. Shealy
is the chief of neurosurgery at the Gunderson Clinic in
LaCrosse, is associated with the neurology sections of
both the University of Wisconsin and the University of
Minnesota, and is widely published in leading medical
journals.

The plan was to put Komar through a battery of
preliminary tests and evaluations in the morning, then
run him through some of the same tests after lunch—
this time while hooked up to various electronic
instruments. Dr. Shealy wanted to measure Komar's
responses to pain on the EEG and EKG machines,
which would track his heart and brain reactions to the
pain stimulation. He also wanted to use a galvanome-
ter to measure skin and muscle response, and a special

instrument for measuring changes in body temperature.

Dr. Shealy began his investigation by assuming that if Komar did not have congenital analgesia (no physical awareness of pain—a rare condition with which certain persons are born), then he probably has considerable ability to control his mind.

A complete neurological work-up was given to Komar. The test results determined that he is a relatively normal subject, both physically and neurologically. He apparently does not have congenital analgesia, and is as sensitive to pain as anybody else. Dr. Shealy observed that Komar had no apparent damage to his back from lying on his bed of nails three times a day during the preceding week. There were marks on his back, but these did not appear to have created punctures.

Following the neurological and physical examinations, Dr. Shealy began the pain response evaluations. He applied a tourniquet to Komar's right arm.

Shutting off the blood can have some persons writhing on the floor in agony after just two minutes. Komar, who said he was disassociating himself from any pain that might occur in his right arm, advised the doctor he felt no discomfort.

Dr. Shealy removed the tourniquet after five minutes and seemed surprised that Komar reported absolutely no pain.

Next, Komar was asked to plunge his arm into a bucket of ice-cold water and see how long he could stand the freezing sensation. Komar withdrew his arm from the water after thirty seconds and said he could not stand it any longer. He was then asked to try the same test again—but this time he was to try to control the pain.

Komar placed his arm back into the freezing water.

Two-and-a-half minutes later, Dr. Shealy withdrew Komar's arm from the ice-water. Komar reported no pain during the second immersion.

The test was followed by the running of a nineteen-gauge needle through Komar's biceps.

Komar willed himself into a trance and reported feeling no pain; as a matter of fact, he didn't even flinch.

Dr. Shealy brought out a battery-powered electric rod that is used to test pain thresholds. The amount of charge can be intensified by advancing a lever on the rod.

Komar was able to withstand the maximum charge without feeling any pain.

After lunch Dr. Shealy continued the testing. The schedule included a rerun of the ice-water test, the needle through the arm, the bed of nails, and Komar's reaction to hypnotic suggestion. Dr. Shealy also wanted to see if Komar could cause body-temperature changes at will.

Tests were made of Komar's responses while he was in a normal state of consciousness and awareness. The complete battery of monitored tests took the better part of an hour.

The results turned out to be what Dr. Shealy had expected. The electronic instruments showed that Komar was able to launch himself into an altered state of consciousness. In this state of mind, he was able to disassociate himself from the pain whenever he wanted.

In discussing the Komar experiments, Dr. Shealy said that "lying on a bed of nails is thought by most individuals to be extremely painful and to require great will power. We fully expected it would require a theta state of brain activity. The obvious physical principle of dispersing a large surface area over a number of nail points prevents serious pain or injury. The minimal discomfort brought about in my bed-of-nails test (with no previous experience) is evidence that the procedure is not a major physical threat. Nevertheless, the ability to stay on such a bed for twenty-five hours or to have 1,142 pounds pressed on the abdomen and chest, demands considerable mind control.

"It is obvious from the ice-water test that Komar has an innate ability to distract his mind by going into at least an alpha state, and in it having control over his autonomic nervous system. Presumably, in his more stress-filled public demonstrations, he uses that state of mind to prevent pain and body damage. There was no sustained theta state in the current experiments."

Dr. Shealy concluded his comments of the tests by saying that Komar, who has had no formal Yoga training and no neurological deficit, *can mentally distract pain from himself.*

Vernon Craig was born in 1932 in Hamilton, Ohio. As a child, he had an interest in rare plants. At one time he had in the family home a collection of rare tropical plants which included 150 orchids and more than 1,000 cacti.

When he was a teenager, Craig found employment with an amusement park near Hamilton. He doubled as a waiter and a magician's assistant, and became an understudy in an aerialist act. He left carnival life to learn cheesemaking, and he was soon promoted to chief cheesemaker.

In spite of success in the cheesemaking business, the future fakir felt the need to work with plants. When he learned that the College of Wooster was looking for a head gardener, he submitted a letter of application and was hired. While he was head gardener, he joined the Wooster, Ohio, Jaycees, serving as chairman of the Mental Health and Retardation Committee.

It was as a member of the Jaycees that Craig was asked to entertain at the barbecue, where his first fire-walking exploit took place. It was another Jaycee project that prompted Komar's attempt to break the existing world's record for lying on a bed of nails. The champion, an Australian, had done it for twenty-five hours, nine minutes; and Komar would be aiming for the astounding time of fifty-six hours!

Komar arrived at the Chamber of Commerce office in Wooster's public square at 7:30 on Thursday morning. Reporters scurried around, jostling for positions that would afford them the best views. At 9:00 a.m. EST, Vernon Craig lay down on his bed of nails.

A crowd gathered. For hours Komar answered their questions via a public-address system. Most of their questions related to the pain, the sharpness of the nails, and "Are you bleeding?"

These questions almost cost the Hindu fakir his record. Needless to say, it is difficult to shut thoughts of pain out of the mind when one is being constantly questioned about that very subject. There is every reason to believe that Komar would have achieved his goal of fifty-six hours if he had been allowed privacy.

Komar rose from his bed of nails at 10:20 plus fifteen seconds on Friday morning, July 13. Although he had not reached his goal of fifty-six hours, he had established a new world record, exceeding the existing time by eleven minutes.

And Komar reported no pain, only a "tingling sensation."

On August 23, 1971, Vernon Craig received a letter from Norris McWhirter, managing editor of the *Guinness Book of World Records* confirming the new world's record. At the time, Komar was listed in *Guinness* as holding the world's record for having the most weight (825 pounds) on him lying on nails. Since then, the Hindu fakir bettered his own record with a figure of 992 pounds, established at the International Aquarian Age Conference held at Honolulu, Hawaii, in February 1972; and with the total of 1,142 pounds set on the *Mike Douglas Show* on March, 1974.

Although Komar's record-breaking session of nail-lying has brought him international fame, he remains modest about his achievement. He describes himself as "an ordinary man who suddenly developed certain abilities."

But how many "ordinary" men are able to lie for hours on a bed of sharpened nails?

Or leap barefooted onto the same kind of "cushion"?

Or walk up a ladder with swords for steps?

Either "ordinary" is badly in need of redefinition, or the vast majority of people are living at a level of self-awareness that is far below ordinary standards. Komar believes the latter to be the case.

"Scientists are saying that most of us use only about ten percent of our mental capacities," declares Craig. "I try to get across to the people who come to see me that it is possible, with proper discipline and training, to utilize much more than ten percent of their minds.

"Through concentration, I must place my body into a state of relaxation in which body tissue becomes more resilient. Once that state is reached, the tissues give, with the result that the nails do not penetrate as deeply as when the body is tense. Many think that the thing to do is to tighten up the muscles, but nothing could be further from the truth."

Komar also declares that he uses no substances to toughen his skin. "That is, unless ordinary soap and water can be called hardening agents."

Some might think of local anesthesia, such as the dentist's Novocaine, as one explanation for Komar's ability to defy pain. Komar denies this, saying that he is able to feel pressure from the hundreds of nails next to his skin, but no pain.

"If, while I am on the nails, someone were to insert their finger between the nails and touch my back, I would know it," Komar explains.

"I maintain this state while I am actually on the nails. But immediately after I get up, if someone were to stick me with a hatpin, I'd probably go straight up.

"In a sense," says Komar, "I out-think the pain. The mind can be disciplined to accept only one sensation at a time. *By filling the mind with another sensation, pain is displaced and the body ceases to react to the painful stimulus.*

"In a more profound sense, what happens during my demonstrations is more like disassociation of mind and body. Just before I jump onto the nails, for example, I pause momentarily, pick out an object a short distance away, then focus my mind on it. At other times I visualize a little ball—sort of a third eye—as I begin. I picture that little ball going out of my head with my mind following."

Komar repeatedly emphasizes that he does not consider himself a mystic or a psychic. Referring to his sensation of being out of the body, he hastens to point out that it is only a sensation, not an actual out-of-body experience.

"I do not picture myself as standing apart watching

the action in an astral body or anything like that. The demonstrations can be frightening. I don't even like to watch the filmed performances on television, although I have done so several times. When I am on the nails, I picture something pleasant or funny.

"Sometimes I feel as if I am lying in a field of flowers, usually daisies or clover. It's a sensational feeling, as if I am free of the body."

Perhaps one reason why Komar does not like to watch his demonstrations on television is because, by his own admission, he has an unusually low tolerance for pain!

"I can hardly walk around without my shoes and socks," says the man who has walked twenty-five feet across a bed of coals hot enough to melt away the legs of his rayon pantaloons. "Even with shoes on, it hurts my feet to walk on a gravel path!"

I asked Komar if he could recreate exactly his mental process as he lay on a bed of nails.

"Through the years, I have programmed my mind," he answered. "Somehow I have a good working system between the subconscious and the conscious; and whenever it's needed, my subconscious takes over.

"Anyone who has attained self-mastery will know exactly what to do in any instance of pain. Usually, and in my case particularly, I stop pain before it even occurs. Most of the pains we're talking about are totally alien to my body, because I've never had them."

"Right now if I would bring out a bed of nails," I asked, "what's the first thing you would think of?"

"The humor of knowing I have to lie on it would put me into a relaxed state of mind." Komar laughed.

"A happy person doesn't have pain! A happy person is a healthy person. I'm in a very positive frame of mind when I lie on the nails. There is an initial sensation. I can't call it pain, but I know the body is being damaged at that point.

"But then the subconscious seems to take over. When 1,100 pounds are on me, I know that they will not puncture my body. I think the subconscious is letting me know.

"There are times when I am about to firewalk when I know I am not ready to go across those coals. If I did at that point, I would be burned. I just know when I am ready.

"I start to walk toward the bed of coals, and if I'm not going to go across them—if I'm not in the right frame of mind—I stop within a couple of steps of the coals. It's happened on only a couple of occasions. I'm aware of people and everything around me, but they can see I'm in a trance-like state to a degree.

"One doctor seems to think I might be down as low as the delta brainwave state at the time I go across the coals. This, he feels, might prevent me from feeling the sensation of pain, but he does not know what would cause me *not* to be burned. This is what is amazing to the medical field. My clothing isn't even affected!

"It might be it's possible to build up a mental field so strong that I can put a layer of 'something' between my feet and the hot coals.

"I feel heat, but yet don't feel it—it's a weird sensation that I cannot adequately describe.

"I cannot talk after I get into that state of mind. I walk around and around the coals, blocking them out to the point where they don't exist anymore. Although they're there, in my mind they don't exist.

"When I get so convinced, I walk a few steps away from the coals, raise my hands to let everybody know I'm coming through, pull up my pantaloons, and start to walk across."

Medical men are interested in the condition of the skin on the Hindu fakir's feet after they have watched his demonstrations. One physician, after a particularly critical examination of Komar's feet, was moved to proclaim that, "There are many who would be happy to have skin like this. His skin is soft as a baby's."

Komar's approach to eating and the use of alcohol can be summarized in one word: Moderation.

He follows no specific diet, but says he is not "heavy on meat." Komar also says he enjoys an occasional social beer.

With reference to sex, Komar follows the same principle: "Moderation must be the rule."

He believes that excessive sexual desire results from "thinking about sex," and in extreme cases becomes an obsession. He believes that excess desire can be controlled by the same method he uses to block pain.

"If it's possible to out-think pain," Komar explains, "it should also be possible to out-think frustration resulting from unsatisfied sexual desire."

He is not, however, so moderate in his attitude toward drugs.

Komar says that he uses no drugs whatsoever, shunning even aspirin. He seldom drinks coffee because he feels that it is too much of a stimulant.

Even though Komar makes no claims of psychic power, he has been encouraged to try healing. Komar says that many psychic sensitives have told him that they feel he has this power, but that he is waiting until he learns more about the subject.

It would appear that he knows more than he admits, because he claims to have kept himself free of sickness for the past twenty years, except for an occasional case of minor "sniffles."

"I can feel illness coming on," Komar says, "and through concentration and relaxation of the body I can ward it off."

Komar has also developed a method of losing weight through mental exercise. Truly a victory of mind over matter—or perhaps over mass.

Komar prefers not to refer to his abilities as paranormal in origin. There are, nevertheless, a number of factors and incidents connected with Vernon Craig's childhood that indicate special properties of mind.

He recalls that his mother was chronically ill and underwent a number of surgical operations for ailments that were probably psychosomatic in origin. Leona Craig tended to be "very religious," of the "hellfire-and-damnation" kind of church-going with its emphasis on sin and suffering.

Orville and Leona Craig were Mormans. Despite his mother's religious propensities, Vernon cannot remember them attending church more than six or eight times. Young Vernon, however, attended a number of different churches with friends, gaining knowledge of the teachings and creed of several denominations.

Craig describes his childhood as lonely. Not having regular playmates, it was most natural for his thoughts to turn inward.

Near Craig's childhood home was a wooded area where he would often seek solitude to meditate and "just think." It was here that the boy destined to become Komar the Hindu Fakir may have experienced moments of clairvoyance.

"I used to see things there in the woods," Craig

muses. "Things like Indian battles and pioneers. Just like we studied in history..."

Craig paused in the middle of his sentence. "Now that I remember," he continued, "that was just about the same time I was having those nightmares. I dreamed of battle scenes; people were being bombed—blown to bits! And in Technicolor! It was horrible. Made me try to stay awake on purpose just to avoid dreaming."

If Craig should someday find that he does have psychic powers, he will not be the first in his family. He relates, with a touch of humor, the story of his "witch aunt."

"She was weird! Aunt Marge even looked like a witch, that is, like the concept I held then of what a witch should look like. She was said to have been born with a veil.

"Aunt Marge was quite good at reading cards and was always telling fortunes for my mother and others. If visitors were coming, she knew about it in advance, and could even give their names. I only saw her two or three times a year, but it was enough to get me interested in the things she did."

Of all the influences that guided the life of Vernon Craig along the pathway that has led to the emergence of Komar, none surpasses in importance his discovery of yoga.

Vernon's father worked in a paper mill where scrap paper was reprocessed into useable form. Vernon recalls that bales of paper were shipped to the mill and that, occasionally, there would be books among them.

One day the eleven-year-old Vernon was visiting the paper mill. In the midst of a bale of reclaimed paper he spotted a book. When he had extricated his find, he saw that it was a book outlining the practice of Yoga, by the noted yogi Ramacharaka.

"I was intrigued," says Craig. "Soon I was practicing the Yoga system of breath control, which I followed for four years." (He adds that he has never studied formally with a yogi, but has talked with many of them, gaining a clearer understanding of what he is doing.)

Is Craig simply an ordinary man who suddenly developed extraordinary abilities?

Is Komar the Hindu Fakir merely a clever showman who knows better than others how to combine illusion with reality?

Is there nothing more to Komar's amazing demonstrations than relaxation, hypnotic analgesia, and knowledge of certain physical principles?

What radical change of mind might cause a man who admits that he can hardly walk around his own front room in his bare feet, and who, even when wearing shoes, avoids gravel paths whenever possible, to invite a thousand people watch him "saunter" across twenty-five feet of live coals?

If one finds Craig's explanation of his abilities inadequate, if one rejects his expressed concept of himself as an ordinary man, it remains to establish answers to these enigmas on other grounds.

Are the mind and body of Vernon Craig taken over by another consciousness for the purpose of getting across a message by means of Komar's demonstrations?

Are the Hindu fakir's abilities the result of a powerful reaction-formation process in Vernon Craig's subconscious mind, given amplified power of expression by the mind-expanding properties of Yoga?

Is Vernon Craig the reincarnation of an advanced Yoga adept, who has acquired his knowledge and abilities as he rides the wheel of Samasara, the merry-go-round of birth and death?

A closer look at Craig's life, especially his youth, reveals events related to all three possibilities. Craig himself has mixed feelings about the significance of his formative years, insisting on the one hand that his was a normal childhood, yet saying in a different context that he believes his "present state" is a development of earlier happenings.

Mention has already been made of Craig's childhood dreams, or "nightmares," as he speaks of them. Although he was frightened by the scenes of battles and bombings, that fear was mild when compared with other images that came to him in the night.

"I don't know whether to call them nightmares," ponders Craig.

"Nightmares are one kind of dream, and usually one dreams when asleep. Sometimes when I saw the faces, I don't know if I was asleep or awake. One of them was much more vivid than the others.

"The face was longer than what we think of as average. The forehead was wide with the rest of the face gradually narrowing to a pointed chin. I wouldn't call it a human face, yet it was human-like. There was something else about that face, above and beyond its unusual shape. Something (why can't I remember *what*?) that it was wearing on its head.

"At the time, I thought of the faces as sinister and evil, but in those days it was customary in our family to regard anything that couldn't be explained as evil.

"Our entire community thought like this, and some were always preaching hell and damnation. I wouldn't be so quick nowadays to describe the face as evil, but it was certainly strange."

Was the "strange" face seen by the youthful Vernon

Craig that of a discarnate entity?

What was the forgotten object worn by this nocturnal visitor?

And what new knowledge caused Craig to revise his childhood evaluation of the face's nature?

It is possible that the faces were products of Craig's rich imagination. We have seen that Vernon's youth was a lonely one. Lacking flesh-and-blood companions, it would have been entirely natural for him to have sought friends in fantasy.

When asked what kind of material comprised his childhood reading, Craig replied:

"I read a lot of comic books. Also anything I could find that had a jungle setting. This was true of the movies, also. I went to see jungle movies and followed serials like *Nyoka the Jungle Girl*. I read the books about Frankenstein, Dracula, and the Wolfman. Bela Lugosi was my favorite male actor. In short, my tastes ran to the weird, the bizarre."

Craig was also attracted to literature and films about India and Egypt. He names the works of Rudyard Kipling, especially *The Jungle Book*. "One of the greatest books I ever read," says Craig, "was H. Rider Haggard's *She*."

Craig remembers that sometimes other children would come to play in the woods. Like children everywhere, Vernon and his friends improvised costumes to go with the characters they portrayed. In the course of this play, the boy who was to become famous as Komar the Hindu Fakir would sometimes fashion a turban.

"At times," Craig says thoughtfully, "I would wear a turban, but I don't remember exactly what for." He hastens to add: "I didn't wear the turban at all times, just now and then."

This information increases in importance when seen in relation to Komar's feelings about his stage costume. Although he has recently performed the firewalk in an ordinary business suit, Komar usually dresses for the part in pantaloons of rich blue rayon, a shirt of flowing golden material, and a dark-colored vest for contrast. Around his waist he wears a leopard-skin cumberbund. Upon his head there flashes a shining white turban.

Vernon Craig explains that Komar's garb had its beginning as a Halloween costume more than twenty years ago.

What inspired Craig to choose the garments of a fakir? He doesn't know.

Speaking of the Halloween party, Craig remarks: "I don't even know what I was supposed to represent. Whatever I was supposed to be, I went about my costuming in earnest. I even wore an earring, which made me feel even more authentic."

Craig does not share Komar's affinity for the earring. He wears only a wristwatch and two favorite rings.

Craig has more to say about Komar's costume:

"My costume completely transformed me into my alter-ego. Until recently I never gave a performance without the costume. There was something in particular about the turban. The turban seemed to be the key to my confidence. Only recently have I been able to dispense with it."

Were the faces that appeared to Vernon Craig those of alien entities seeking a mind and body to possess?

Is it possible that the young Craig, with his obviously expanded consciousness, sensed their purpose and that this might be the real reason why he conceived of them as evil?

Living as he did in a home and community where "hellfire and damnation" religion characterized the spiritual aspect of life, it is highly probable that Craig had heard the New Testament accounts of demon possession. To those who derive their concepts of spirit control solely from that source, the mere thought would be enough to engender an overwhelming sense of terror.

Even if they are aware of its existence, it is certain that the fire and brimstone varieties of theologians do not mention that the Greek word from which the Anglo-Saxon word "demon" is derived has as one of its primary meanings "genius" or familiar, tutelary spirit. In other words, a source of inspiration, a servant, and a teacher.

Craig asserts that he can give a logical explanation for the things he does during his demonstrations, with the exception of firewalking. There are details, however, for which Craig cannot logically account. He cannot explain his life-long interest in the Orient, nor remember his reasons for wearing a turban during childhood games.

Why did Vernon Craig design what is now Komar's costume for a Halloween party not knowing at the time what role he had chosen? And how many persons would have their ears pierced for an earring simply to make a costume for a single event more authentic?

Although he says that he has no realization of assuming another identity, Craig sometimes refers to Komar as if he were a separate entity.

In a newspaper article by Rick Van Sant of UPI, Craig is quoted as saying:

"I've developed a split personality. Komar has become my alter-ego."

In a letter to the producer of a popular TV show,

Craig thanks him for "using Komar" on a show.

Are these merely ways of speaking, or are there more profound reasons for Craig to refer to Komar as a nearly separate entity?

All of us have at times said and done things or suffered lapses of memory contrary to conscious intentions or purposes. In most of these cases there is no need to look for profound explanations, either from psychological or psychic sources; but when someone goes against his conscious intent to the degree which Craig did when he invited the barbecue guests to watch him walk on hot coals, one cannot help wondering what power prompted such a reversal.

Control by an alien entity is one possible answer, but it is also possible that the prompting came from within, the result of Craig's expanded mental processes.

"I use Yoga," explains Craig, "the power of positive thinking, and perhaps a form of self-hypnosis. A combination of ingredients, you might say."

Craig's combination of ingredients can be, in turn, combined into one method. All three of the systems he names are directed toward the goal of influencing the subconscious mind to work in a particular way, of going beyond the limitations set upon the mind by various conditioning factors.

Perhaps some would speak of Komar's feats as demonstrations of mind over matter. Considering his own description, perhaps mind *out* of matter would be more fitting.

The fact that Vernon Craig pictures himself as being in a place other than the location of Komar's demonstration presents an additional enigma in view of the fact that he does not enter a state of trance during his demonstrations. He points out that he can carry on conversations while on the nails. On the other hand some doctors have stated their suspicion that Komar is *always* in the alpha state.

It is difficult to talk to Vernon Craig about his life and career as Komar without returning again and again to the subject of reincarnation.

Although Craig lays no claim to being the present incarnation of a Hindu fakir, yogi, or swami, and he remains skeptical toward the doctrine of reincarnation itself, his statements reveal not only a knowledge of the subject, but a conscious pattern that to some extent contradicts his expressions of doubt.

Craig speaks constantly of his fascination with things of an Oriental nature, yet gives no indication of how this fascination originated. Certainly there was not much in the "hellfire and damnation" brand of religion that was promulgated in his childhood home and community to encourage interest in peoples and customs which were most surely dismissed as "heathen."

In addition to an interest in the Orient, the young Vernon Craig was drawn strongly to stories with a jungle setting.

Was it memories of a land of trees, vines, and flowers that led Craig to become interested in horticulture, an interest that pre-dated even his discovery of Yoga?

And was it a sense of the familiar that led him to the woods to meditate and to receive some of the earliest indications of the extraordinary powers of mind he was destined to develop?

In the case of Komar, reincarnation is a more plausible explanation than possession. When an alien entity takes control of a living person, it does not claim to be a former incarnation of the subject. In cases of apparent reincarnation, on the other hand, the entity speaks of a former life, not a period of temporary control.

When Craig is performing as Komar, he retains his own appearance, mannerisms, and tone of voice, as opposed to cases of possession in which the subject often undergoes changes of features, behavior, and speaks with the voice of the possessing entity. The fact that the Hindu fakir has no memories or intimations of a previous existence can be explained by the Hindu belief that one should not try, or be encouraged to try, to remember former incarnations. The Hindus believe to do so is to bring about an early death and incurrence of bad Karma.

The same dogma may be responsible for Vernon Craig's attitude toward the paranormal aspects of his abilities. Is his skepticism a mask for his reluctance to pursue the subject, lest he remember the reasons for things for which he now says he has no explanation, or for which he offers logical ones?

It is interesting to note that although Craig professes a life-long fascination for jungles, he says emphatically that he would not like to visit one.

Does this contradiction relate in any way to what seems to be the nearest thing to a recurring dream that Craig remembers?

Referring to his childhood dreams, Craig recalls: "I was always running away from something."

It has already been mentioned that Komar, before making his leap onto the nails, chooses an object in the distance upon which to focus his mind. Is his dream of fleeing related to the fact that an object that Komar frequently uses in this manner is an "Exit" sign?

Craig says that as a child he lay awake many nights because he feared to dream.

Today Craig says that he doesn't dream very much, "at least dreams that I remember. Sometimes I go for as long as one year without remembering a dream. Usually, the only times that I dream are when I sleep for longer periods of time than I am accustomed."

If Craig does not remember his dreams, it is likely that it is because he doesn't want to. It is not unusual to have recurring dreams, but it is rare, to say the least, to hear of continuous dreams. Even rarer is the individual who can break off a dream and then pick it up again without breaking its continuity. Craig declares that he can do just that.

"If I have an interesting dream, one that I want to continue, I can pick it up again the next night, or the same night if I am awakened. I can pick up a dream the second night, and even the third, or for as long as I wish to continue the dream. When I no longer wish to continue, I simply turn the dream off."

Many are able to remember incidents from their infancy and early childhood. But how many can describe in detail an event that took place before birth?

"When I was about seven years old," relates Vernon Craig, "I spoke to my mother about a fishing and camping trip that I remembered.

"My mother said to me, 'You couldn't remember that trip. It happened before you were born.'

"But I went on to describe it to her in detail. It was not that I simply remembered the trip, it was like I could see it."

It seems reasonable to postulate that an individual who has learned to control to such an extent his subconscious mind would be capable of exercising his ability to recall past lives.

Craig says that he is not a "firm believer" in

reincarnation, but he does believe it to be a subject worthy of continuing study.

"During recent years," he discloses, "I have heard more and more about reincarnation. A medical doctor who believes very strongly in rebirth told me that I couldn't possibly have acquired the knowledge and ability to do the things I do during one lifetime.

"I had to learn somewhere, because in the beginning I just jumped in and started lying on nails, leaping on nails, walking on the edges of swords, and, on one occasion, strolled across a bed of hot coals. Certainly these are phenomena usually associated with yogis, swamis, fakirs, and other adepts native to the Orient.

"Still, as of this time, I have no clearly defined reason to believe that I am the reincarnation of an Oriental adept or of anything else. But be assured that I am continuing to seriously study the subject."

When Vernon Craig first started his demonstrations, he used his own name in the billings. Resplendent in his costume of blue and gold, accented by a waistband of leopard skin and wearing a white turban, Craig looks more like an Oriental potentate than a fakir.

"Fakir" is a transliteration of an Arabic word meaning "needy person," referring to man's need of God. Fakirs are regarded as holy men who possess the power to work miracles. They are related to the dervishes, which are found only within the sect of Islam known as Sufis. It is thought that Omar Khayyam, the eleventh-century Persian poet, was at one period of his life a Sufi.

The Rubaiyat of Omar Khayyam has long been linked to Hedonism, a branch of philosophy that teaches that the purpose of life is pleasure, be it sensual, intellectual, or spiritual. In ancient Greece the Epicureans developed a form of negative Hedonism that emphasized the fact that every pleasure had its attendant pain, and that the ideal life was to be found, not in positive enjoyment, but in cultivating an attitude of indifference to pain.

Is there a relationship between the Epicureans' teachings and the pain-defying demonstrations of Komar?

Was it an unconscious memory that influenced Craig to use elements of Omar Khayyam's name to form that of his alter-ego?

Could it be that "jungle" somehow symbolizes the world for Craig in the same way that the Persian poet used "wilderness"?

Pythagoras, who brought the doctrine of rebirth from Asia to Greece, was born on the Island of Samos, also the birthplace of Epicurus. There can be no doubt that reincarnation was accepted by Omar Khayyam and his contemporaries.

In Quatrain XLIV of the *Rubaiyat,* Omar refers to the physical body as a "clay carcase." In Quatrain XLV the poet declares:

> Tis but a tent where takes his rest
> A sultan to the realm of death addrest;
> The sultan rises, and the dark Ferrash
> Strikes, and prepares for another guest.

No matter what aspect of Vernon Craig's life one examines, there is in evidence the influence of the Orient. With the interesting exceptions of merry-go-round music and music-box sounds, Craig's favorite music all has an Eastern motif. Two selections he mentions in particular are *Scheherazade* and *East of Suez.* Oddly enough, the Hindu fakir does not favor music played on the sitar, saying that it is "too classical."

His preference for clothing runs to loose-fitting, casual styles, and he says that at home he wears "nothing but a robe" a great deal of the time. He admires the attire of the ancient Egyptians as depicted in books and motion pictures, and the garment made famous by Dorothy Lamour; the sarong. Craig discloses that he is "most comfortable in the costume he wears when performing as Komar."

Having considered the enigma of Komar the Hindu Fakir from the standpoints of possession, power of the subconscious mind, and reincarnation, we return to the man himself. Is Vernon Craig really an ordinary man who has learned to do extraordinary things?

He speaks of Komar as his alter-ego, but at no time does he assume or pretend to assume a separate identity.

Although deeply interested in reincarnation, Craig says that he has no clearly defined reason to believe that he is the present incarnation of anyone but himself.

Everything else notwithstanding, he maintains that his amazing feats are accomplished through the observance of physical principles, complete relaxation of the body, and mental blocking of pain.

After four years of practicing Yoga, Craig discovered that by varying the rhythmic patterns, he became able to perform different acts. He uses one pattern for lying on nails, another for leaping on nails, and others for different parts of his demonstrations. So deeply has Craig impressed these patterns upon his mind that he does not have consciously to remember to vary the breathing patterns.

"The fact is," Craig asserts, "the entire demonstration is performed at the subconscious level. As the number of demonstrations per day or per week increases, so does my sensitivity to pain. This means that I must exercise more concentration to block the pain, but even this is regulated without conscious thought."

The fact that a man occasionally has daydreams is not evidence of the presence of paranormal powers. But if those daydreams take the form of prophecies of events that are still in the future, that is something else again.

Komar is in the habit of lying down between demonstrations for brief periods of rest, and it was during these periods that he began to "daydream" about future events. Friends encouraged him to write down his predictions, which proved to be so accurate that Komar has come to be included in lists of seers asked to furnish predictions for newspapers and books on prophecy.

Despite the number of "hits" Komar has made with his prophecies, he does not claim clairvoyant powers, adding that "anyone can make predictions if they give it a little thought." Komar reports, nevertheless, that he is learning to turn on his prophetic daydreams by means of concentration on particular subjects.

It is perhaps from a deeper understanding of man's true nature that Komar speaks when he refers to himself as "ordinary." Perhaps his meaning will become clear when, in retrospect, men of the future consider our present concepts of man in the same light as we consider those of men of the Stone Age.

Komar insists that his feats are accomplished by known mental processes. It is his intent to teach others how they may enlarge their scope of self-knowledge by pushing back the barrier between the two compartments of the human mind.

Komar believes that his system can be used to facilitate natural childbirth, to cure the common cold, and to control pain. In order to best accomplish this, Komar says that he utilizes demonstration methods with his lectures, because "... demonstrations literally shock people into the realization that they live their entire lives without using ninety percent of their mental capacities."

In men like Komar it is possible that we have a living prediction of the ordinary man of the future, enlarged and enhanced in nearly all of his capacities.

CHAPTER 1

The Merciful Goal of Pain Control: Komar's Own Observations

As I travel around the United States, Canada, and Great Britain, presenting my demonstrations of pain control, I continually hear men and women describing their pain as "stabbing," "wrenching," "burning," "pulsing," "dull, but steady," and any number of other adjectives of misery and agony.

For the great majority of people, pain is a relatively brief ordeal in their otherwise healthy lives. But there are millions of men and women for whom chronic pain has become neither a major nor minor symptom—it has become a debilitating disease in itself.

Such a sad state need not exist. Pain control may be

attained by every man and woman willing to invest a few minutes a day practicing mental and physical exercises.

Medical science is currently in the process of perfecting a number of mechanical devices to treat chronic pain. There are now seventeen pain clinics in the United States, and many hospitals support their own pain units. At these various clinics and institutions, pain is being met by electrical transcutaneous stimulators, surgical nerve blocks, radio waves, drugs, acupuncture, biofeedback training, and hypnosis.

These devoted pain specialists, called dolorologists, usually agree that there is both an emotional and a physical component to pain. Personality maladjustments may have to be dealt with before any successful healing technique might be accomplished.

I must clarify that one must not confuse chronic pain with acute pain.

Acute pain occurs when a bone is fractured, a body part is pierced by a sharp instrument, or some section of the anatomy is burned. Once such wounds have been treated and given a time to mend, the pain goes away.

Chronic pain, though, is seemingly endless, apparently untreatable, and remains to torment its victim long after the original affliction has disappeared.

According to Dr. John J. Bonica, president of the International Association for the Study of Pain, chronic pain costs society about $50 billion a year in medical expenses, lost wages, and worker-compensation benefits.

Other dolorologists have noted that men and women with back pain, the most common chronic symptom, account for more than 18 million medical-office calls a year. Those who suffer chronic headache problems spend more than 12 million hours seeing their medical advisors.

In this book I am primarily concerned with chronic pain, and I am convinced that the natural method of dealing with such pain is of greater personal benefit to the individual than is the application of drugs or mechanical devices.

The techniques which I shall teach you also have the advantage over the external methods in that there are no prescriptions to fill, no equipment to purchase or to carry on the person, and no batteries to malfunction or to wear out.

What is most important to my method is that each reader who is seeking surcease from his or her pain will seriously practice the "Six Steps to Self-Mastery," which I will detail in the next chapter. Once one has mastered his mind and the proper functioning of his body, pain control becomes assured. Right thinking and a positive attitude are extremely important to banishing chronic pain from one's life.

Dr. Steven F. Brena, of the Emory Pain Control Center in Atlanta, has observed that nearly everyone who comes to their clinic has suffered pain that began with an organic condition, but then some personality maladjustment seized upon the advantages to be enjoyed in illness.

"Those who have long-standing emotional problems learned in childhood to use pain as an escape route," Dr. Brena commented.

Dr. Nathaniel R. Hollister, neurologist at the Massachusetts General Hospital, found that pain is "... something more than a response by a person to injury to his body. Pain is actually a learned form of behavior."

Dr. Gerald M. Aronoff, director of the Pain Unit at

Massachusetts Rehabilitation Hospital, said, "We look at life stresses and try to understand why the patient has not gotten well."

Dr. Aronoff and his teams of health-care specialists have found that chronic pain has often sprouted from seeds planted by childhood emotional problems. Once those deep-rooted problems have been identified, the unit utilizes techniques which teach "well behavior."

Too often men and women may actually be rewarded for harboring chronic pain. As long as they nurture their suffering, they are not expected to exert themselves in carrying out life's distasteful tasks. Family members, friends, and co-workers demonstrate their sympathy by taking out the garbage, cleaning the house, lifting the heavier packing crates, accepting extra workloads, or whatever. For some men and women it has paid off to keep a chronic pain.

But when they have eventually grown weary of their suffering, and decided that no amount of sympathy can compensate for chronic pain, they have fallen under the care of too many doctors who have treated *chronic* pain as *acute* pain and gotten their patients into real trouble by prescribing morphine and other addictive drugs.

Or, as Dr. C. Norman Shealy of the Pain and Health Rehabilitation Center in La Crosse, Wisconsin, has woefully observed, the doctors resort too rapidly to surgery.

There are several hundred thousand operations done each year for the treatment of low-back pain. Up to 40 percent of the patients who undergo such corrective surgery, according to Dr. Shealy, fail to obtain relief. In fact, Dr. Shealy points out, the process of the surgery can leave the patient with scar tissue which may only increase the pain.

The April 25, 1977, issue of *Newsweek* reported the following grim statistics:

"The average chronic-pain patient has suffered for seven years, undergone from three to five major operations, and spent from $50,000 to $100,000 in doctors' bills. In between the operations, he has taken countless drugs—from tranquilizers and muscle relaxants to potent narcotics—and there is at least a 50–50 chance that he has acquired a drug habit along the way."

Such techniques and biofeedback seem to be a compromise between self-mastery and our space-age dependency upon machines.

In biofeedback, the electronic amplification of biological signals—i.e., breathing, heart rate—assist one in training the mind to control the body. Although the medical profession does not yet understand how biofeedback training works, it seems that once a patient can see or hear the result of what is going on inside his head and his body, he seems to be able to change it physically.

My friend Dr. David R. Walker of Northern Lights College, St. John, British Columbia, has explained biofeedback and its positive implications in this manner:

> ... You have long been aware that you can control the muscles of your hand, arm and leg ... As an infant and later as a child you had to notice and coordinate all of the signals which came from the object you touched and the muscles which moved your hands and eye and held your body upright.
>
> Because the body is so elegantly constructed, this type of control was easily mastered and was

great fun. However, you stopped short of your potential. You neglected the fact that inside your body there is a universe of muscles and glands whose control is as important as those through which you contact the outside world.

...All of us know of the feats of yogis and adepts; we have all heard of miraculous cures; we have all heard of heroic pain defying feats of persons who have saved loved ones from disasters. These messages have been neglected.

No one is to blame for this past neglect. We came by it honestly.

In the first place, science pointed out that the internal organ systems could run automatically to correct imbalances, to provide stores for the future and to eliminate excesses. Furthermore if the system failed someone else was supposed to be able to fix it.

In the second place, science created an extraordinarily wide variety of things which made us feel insignificant and made us feel that we had no direct control over ourselves.

Finally, to make up for our insignificance, science gave us a tremendous number of toys whose pursuit kept us so busy we had no time or energy left to devote to our internal world.

...At the present time a very large number of us receive only one kind of information about our internal workings. That information is called *pain*. As a messenger pain is very slow—it arrives long after other signals have died at the threshold of our mind. When it comes it commands our attention. Unfortunately, we usually do not treat it properly.

At first pain may be "minor," and because of

this and the tendency to favor our consciousness of the external world, we try to cut off this feedback signal. We open the medicine cabinet so that we can continue the pursuit of our pain-producing life-style; this is obviously a mistake but to make matters worse we even go one step further. We begin to look for the earliest signs of pain so that we can take our painkillers as early as possible. This becomes a vicious cycle in which we become better and better at detecting pain; and, more seriously, we become better and better at creating the conditions which produce it.

Of course it sounds paradoxical to say that our attention to pain will produce more of it, but recent research has shown this to be true. The type of research in which we examine the way in which we learn to produce a variety of changes in bodily processes is called biofeedback.

Biofeedback research has shown that humans can change the activity of many bodily processes. All that is required is that the trainee be *made aware* of the body process in question and be *interested* in this awareness. In the clinic this is used in a very positive way; ordinary people learn to eliminate a variety of conditions ranging from migraine headache to high blood pressure!

For example, a man with serious high blood pressure has his blood pressure monitored by a machine which converts blood pressure changes into sounds or numbers. He is thus made aware that sometimes the pressure is lower than it is at other times. Only his interest, his awareness of his blood pressure, and his desire to control blood pressure are required to make his body produce the conditions associated with lowered blood pressure. At first the man will need the feedback from the blood pressure machine, but after practice he will be on his own; his own mind will be aware of variations in his blood pressure and will know how to keep this pressure low.

Simply by receiving feedback, made possible through sensitive electronic devices, humans have been able to control the activity of many organs which can be involved in a wide variety of common, but serious, ailments. These include heart rate, blood flow, acid secretion, muscle tension, and the electrical activity of the brain itself.

In each case of learned control of bodily activity, the critical ingredients are awareness of the state of the body (at first through the help of a biofeedback machine), interest in this feedback, and the desire to achieve self-control.

This is the critical lesson of biofeedback: The body seeks the awareness of the mind. The body will produce for us the conditions in which we are most interested. This is a two-edged sword; we can live in pain and pessimism or in health and optimism.

. . . Biofeedback clearly shows that we can be the authors of our health, but it also shows us that we have let the situation become serious; our feeling has been reduced to the point that we now need machines to get positive information about ourselves. But we must not fall into the trap of feeling badly about this state of affairs; only by nurturing what is good can goodness itself be increased.

We can look forward to a day when our children will easily dwell on the positive aspects of what is within and around them. At that time the use of machines for feedback will be over. Right now, they invite us to hasten their obsolescence.

I am pleased that Dr. Walker advocates the obsolescence of biofeedback machines, rather than our growing dependence upon them; for I am convinced that self-mastery, rather than habitual dependency on electrical stimulators, drugs, or surgery, is the key to complete and totally beneficial pain control.

What does a natural system of pain control require in terms of an investment on the part of those who are seeking comfort and the elimination of their agony?

As Dr. Gerald M. Aronoff once remarked, "You must spend half an hour a day on yourself. Spend it on relaxation and introspection. Relax those muscles. Get in tune with yourself. Try to understand better what is going on, emotionally, inside you. And keep trying."

Dr. Aronoff has provided us with good advice. Now I will demonstrate how I believe that we can best put such wisdom into practice through the application of the Six Steps to Self-Mastery.

CHAPTER 2

The Six Steps to Self-Mastery

Strange is our situation here upon Earth. Each of us comes for a short visit, not knowing why, yet sometimes seeming to have a divine purpose.

From the standpoint of daily life, however, there is one thing we do know: That man is here for the sake of other men ... for the countless unknown souls with whose fate we are connected by a bond of sympathy.

Many times a day I realize how much my own outer and inner life is built upon the labors of my fellowmen, both living and dead, and how earnestly I must exert myself to give in return as much as I have received and am still receiving.—*Albert Einstein*

I am an ordinary man who has managed to unlock the secrets of pain control.

When I am not performing dramatic demonstrations of pain mastery, I am working in an Ohio cheese factory, not secluding myself away in a Himalayan monastery.

I am an average man with average physical abilities. *If I could learn to control pain, then so can you!*

When man thinks of himself as human, he places limitations upon himself.

But when man thinks of himself as a god, he gains unlimited abilities and control over both his mental and physical health, and over any pain which might threaten his general well-being.

Man is a god—or at least has the potential to become a god.

But mankind has forgotten how to use so many inherent powers. Through the development of mind and body, today's men and women are able to regain these abilities.

Through my lifetime involvement with mankind, I have learned how to apply many of the universal truths as taught by all the great masters of the past. I have used many of these truths in my work with mental retardation, mental illness, and with men confined to penal institutions.

As I worked with so-called "normal people," I discovered that they, too, were only using from 2 to 10 percent of the brain power available to them. That is when I set out to prove through my demonstrations that all men and women are somewhat mentally retarded, due to the fact that they are not using the full potential of their brain power. There are universal steps toward the development of god-like stature in which people may develop themselves to the point where they feel no unnecessary pain, no stress, no torment due to emotional factors.

People bog themselves down with worry about trivia. The average man and woman worries about yesterday and tomorrow—the past and the future— and cannot see what is happening to them today.

Everyone must learn to make the most of now.

Yesterday is past and can never be regained.

Tomorrow will take care of itself.

If you seek to control the pain and afflictions which offend your body, then you must start living in the present.

The first step toward pain control is a recognition that you must learn to relax mind and body together.

When you are able to do this, you will find peace of mind. You will become a healthier individual, and you will find your true position in the ever-moving stream of life.

Once you find that wonderful peace of mind within yourself, you will realize that both personal and external problems may be neutralized through the peace which abounds within.

Before a person was born into the world, his world did not exist. He created his own world.

If, therefore, you live in what you consider an ugly, cruel world, then you have, in essence, created that world for yourself. Your world is ugly and cruel because that's the way you want it.

If you hate yourself, then you also hate everyone else.

The essence of love—and the first step toward pain control—must begin within each person.

Just as I learned to master pain so that I can walk unharmed through red-hot coals, or lie unmarked on beds of nails, so can you learn to control the pain of backache, arthritis, headache, or any other affliction that might decrease your full enjoyment of life.

Everything about your pain is not bad. Pain is a danger signal—an alert. It can be like an internal alarm going off to warn you that a fire may be raging someplace where you may not have checked recently.

It is not that we want to eliminate your body's ability to transmit pain signals. But there is no use in suffering needlessly, especially when the cause of the pain may present little actual danger to the overall health of the body.

Sometimes the stresses of daily living, the many tensions one experiences on the job, or the fear of there being something seriously wrong with the body can magnify the pain signals out of all proportion to the actual reason for the transmissions.

And as I have repeatedly pointed out, there are all too many instances where certain stresses and tensions can so work upon the imagination, and upon certain psychic needs of an individual, that pain can be created when there is no need for a danger signal of any kind.

Perhaps the crux of what I am saying is this: We must first understand that pain is the body's natural danger signal. When we have sought medical aid to alleviate as many of the true danger signals as possible, then there is no purpose in suffering needlessly from pain. Instead, we can learn to control pain—and, in many instances, eliminate completely those signals which originate from stressful situations in our lives.

Today's medical science has established the fact that anywhere from 60 to 90 percent of the pain that men and women suffer lies in their minds; and it's caused by frustration, depression, worries, emotional stresses. Subconsciously, too many men and women simply do not have the desire to rise above their sicknesses.

If a man or woman believes he has nothing to live for, if he simply goes about a day-to-day routine complaining about everything imaginable, then pain and illness will soon become a part of his life.

Mastery of self, once attained, will control pain. Through self-mastery, a person will become better in every aspect of life.

If we learn how to control physical pain, we can also learn how to control emotional pain and face the problems and disappointments of life with a more positive attitude.

So many men and women apparently wish to achieve a full exercise of psychic abilities, healing abilities, and self-control of pain; but people fail to realize that once they have achieved mastery of themselves, they will have all these abilities at their command.

These are universal truths. They will yield the self-mastery necessary to control all pains and afflictions of the physical body:

1. *EGO*—the magic of believing in oneself.
2. *POSITIVE ATTITUDE*—which is so much more than merely positive thinking.
3. *RELAXATION*—which goes hand in hand with physical exercise: Without first tuning the body, it is difficult to tune the mind.
4. *PROPER BREATHING*—the Yogic breathing techniques of complete breath and rhythmic breathing, which everyone can learn, and which, once accomplished, will put each individual well toward the goal of pain control.
5. *CONCENTRATION*—the ability to focus

the mind and remove it from external tensions.

6. *MEDITATION*—a passive form of concentration. Most people never achieve this state. It is the sheer ecstasy of being in tune with the subconscious, the superconscious, the universe, or the godself, whichever has the better meaning to the individual.

CHAPTER 3

Ego:
Master of the Mental States

When I mention the word "ego," many people shudder. A number of counselors and teachers try to tell men and women that they should not have ego.

When I am talking about ego, I am talking about many things. I am not telling a person to be egotistical or self-centered. By ego, I am talking about that little magic of believing in oneself, the ability to love oneself.

In his *Hindu Yoga Science of Breath,* Yogi Ramacharaka says of ego:

"Remember always that the ego is master of the mental states and habits, that the will as the direct instrument of the ego is already ready for its use. Let your soul be filled with a strong desire to cultivate those mental habits that will make you strong. Nature's plan is to produce strong individual expressions of herself. She will be glad to give you her aid in becoming strong. The man who wishes to strengthen himself will always find great forces within him to aid in the work, for is he not carrying out one of nature's pet plans and one for which he has been striving throughout the ages? Anything that tends to make you realize and express your mastery tends to strengthen you and places at your disposal nature's aid. You may witness this in everyday life. Nature seems to like strong individuals and delights in pushing them ahead. By mastery we mean mastery over your own lower nature, as well as over outside nature, of course. The 'I' is master, forget it not, O, student, and assert constantly."

You must learn to accept and to strive for that "I" that is within you. And, once again, you will gain the proper kind of self-love within. It will swell out and show and reveal itself to the world. You will not have to run around and tell everybody, "I love you; I love you," because when you love yourself, it shows that you love the rest of the world, as well.

You must learn to believe in yourself because, if you do not, you cannot convince anyone in the world to believe in you.

When you start to believe that you can accomplish things—that you can be whatever you want to be— then you have begun to believe in yourself.

As you believe in yourself, you will gain a beautiful outlook on life and become more a part of the world. Instead of being in the world, you will become *part* of it. This is highly essential. The mind is the working tool of the ego. Work and strive toward this development.

As children we are programmed to believe in

various things in regard to our world. This often leads to what I call "environmental retardation." We must make the first move and begin to change our world. If our world is not a happy one, we must change it. This is all a part of ego, because each of us has the ability to create a wonderful world and to live in a wonderful world.

But you, and you alone, are the only one who can do that, because you are the only one who lives in your own individual world.

I do not live in your world. No one else lives in your world—unless you want them to live there with you. If those persons you admit into your world are very negative individuals, then they will have an influence on your world and make it an unhappy world once again.

Ask yourself, "What do I really think of myself?"

If your answer is, "Not much," then it's high time you set as your goal the systematic and continued development of self-esteem and the strengthening of your ego.

CHAPTER 4

The Power of Positive Attitude

You must have a positive attitude. You must learn to be positive within every molecule of your body.

Negative thoughts can cause almost any kind of illness—ulcers, blindness, paralysis. On some occasions, negative thinking has even produced death.

If you will yourself into a negative situation, you can become very ill. Start now building your ego to produce positive thoughts—even if you have to go to the point of getting away from family and friends who are very negative. You must learn to have a positive attitude around you at all times.

A little bit of negativity is not bad; it does make the

world interesting. But you must have little goals that you set and reach in order to keep building yourself all the time.

You must not be afraid to strive for goals for yourself that might seem impossible to you right now.

Positive attitude will lead you to expect the most of yourself as an individual and as a human being: This is short and simple, but true.

CHAPTER 5

Body Balance with
Relaxation and Exercise

You must learn to relax mind and body together. You must learn how to get the mind into a sleeplike state while you are totally awake. It is in this state that you have control over the will and the body; but you must be able to relax both of them together.

Relaxation goes hand in hand with physical exercise. You must learn to tone your body and stimulate adequate blood circulation. Good circulation also helps to eradicate pain.

The daily routines of most men and women in our society, whether on the farm or in the factory, do not really keep them in A-1 condition. Normal work activities usually exercise only part of the body. One must select an activity vigorous enough to get the neglected parts of the body into working order, thereby affecting the circulatory system and developing and strengthening the muscles of the heart. By forcing blood to the arteries and veins at a rapid pace, they are kept pliable and very responsive.

All parts of your body are interrelated and connected and function as a whole. The mind cannot be separated from the body.

As you begin to feel better physically, your mind will follow right along; and you will find yourself discovering increased self-awareness, increased self-confidence, and improved mental tone.

Good health is either a gift of our parents or the result of a life-style that suits our evolutionary history.

When anyone learns how to relax both mind and body together, it is amazing how his or her outlook changes and how one's health improves. Society is responsible for much of our sickness and pain. We have become so goal-oriented that everything we do must have a utilitarian purpose. Such an unceasingly material attitude can make one miss the value of each moment.

Here are some simple calisthenics that anyone can do, which I have outlined in seven basic movements.

The *first* is the side push, both left and right.

Stand in a half-crouching position, placing the clenched fist of your right hand on your chest.

Extend the right hand and arm up and out. Open the fingers very wide. Lower the arm in a semi-circle while bringing the hand to the chest, closing the hand tightly as it touches the chest. Do the same with the left arm and hand.

At the same time, move up and down alternately on your toes. This will tend to rock you back and forth. Breathe deeply with the movements.

The *second* movement is the body twist.

In the same half-crouching position, put the clenched fist on the chest, extend the right hand, and swing around to the right as far as you can go, opening the hand and fingers. Swing back, return the hand to your chest, closing the fist.

Now do the same thing with the left hand. Take deep breaths as you swing to the right, and expel as you swing to the left.

Twist and contort the muscles of the face with both movements.

In the *third* and *fourth* movements, begin in a half-crouching position.

Put your clenched fists on the chest, extend both hands and arms parallel up to the right, then down, and then up, making a complete circle, bringing both closed hands back to the chest.

Do this a number of times and reverse, starting up and to the left, breathing hard with each movement, and continue to twist and contort the face muscles.

Movement number *five* is up and down and straight forward.

This calls for bending of the knees. Stand straight, clench both fists, and hold them shoulder-high. Reach up with both arms forward, then bring them down. As you go down, bend the knees as far as possible so that when the hands come down, they nearly touch the floor.

Complete the movement, bringing the hands (which

were open in the swing) back to the shoulder-high position, tightly closed. Take a deep breath on the downswing and expel as you complete the upward swing to the original position.

Exercise the facial muscles as instructed before. Facial-muscle exercises keep your face very youthful. They eradicate wrinkles.

The five steps that I have presented thus far are basic exercises which condition the circulatory system. In developing these steps, the following suggestions should be noted:

1. Follow the instructions carefully and work out the pattern for each one. In the beginning this will go slowly; but after a short time the pattern will become automatic, so it will not require much thought.

2. With the exception of movement number five, start from a crouching position and move as much as possible on the toes to strengthen the arches and muscles of the feet as well.

3. In the beginning, do the exercises *only a few times* so that you do not put undue stress on the heart. *Never* jump into an exercise program and overdo it the first few days.

4. Be sure to include all elements in these exercises—half-crouching on the toes, opening and closing hands vigorously with each movement, taking deep breaths with each movement and expelling fully, twisting and contorting the muscles of the face in all exercises. Build up speed and gradually, but eventually, make the exercise fast enough so that in three minutes' time you will *gently* punish yourself.

Movement *six* emphasizes the head and neck roll. This exercise is intended to loosen up the muscles, arteries, and veins of the neck and shoulders, all of which directly affect the ears, eyes, and throat, and other organs of the body.

Sitting up straight, drop your head forward onto the chest. Then, without lifting the head, start to roll it to the left, up and over the left shoulder and over the back as far as possible, then over the right shoulder and down.

In doing this roll, extend your head as far as possible. After a few rolls to the left, making a complete circle, reverse and go to the right.

This is a good exercise, incidentally, for those who are doing long-distance driving. Stop the car occasionally, go through the exercise, knead your shoulders and neck with thumb and fingers, and you will find that you become alert again.

Movement number *seven* emphasizes exercises for the eye muscles.

A friend of mine used this method for training the eyes to wear glasses, and now his vision has improved so much he does not need his glasses anymore! You need muscles to focus the eyes, and that's the reason for these exercises. If they are kept in good condition, you will improve your eyesight and protect the eyes from disease.

The exercises are very, very simple.

1. Move your eyes in the sockets up and down—straight up and straight down.

2. Move them left and right.

3. Move them at an angle from upper right to lower left.

4. Reverse the angle from upper left to lower right.

5. Rotate the eyes in the sockets, starting to the

right and making a circle, then reverse the rotation.

6. Holding a thumb close to the face (about two to three inches from the nose), look at the thumb and then at something in the distance. Keep changing focus from thumb to distance for a short time rather rapidly.

Spend at least two or three minutes each morning and night on these exercises. You need not spend more than ten or fifteen minutes a day on the total program.

For example, you might do the exercises for three minutes on the first five basic movements in the morning, two minutes of the same in the evening, then add three or four more minutes both morning and night for the head roll.

Once you have found how to exercise the body properly and put your muscles in tone, you will truly be ready to learn how to relax, which is the key in my total method of self-mastery. Relaxation relieves tensions, and this is essential for pain control.

I have learned an excellent method of relaxation, which begins by lying flat on the floor.

As you lie on the floor, start breathing very deeply and evenly. Start to relax the muscles of the body. Do not just lie there and say that the muscles are going to relax. Start with the tip of your toes and *tell* them to relax.

Move up to the foot, the ankle, the thigh, etc.; and as you move up higher on your anatomy, tell your muscles to relax.

Mentally say to them, "Muscles in the thigh, relax!" As you move up the body, name every part of your anatomy to the very tiptop of your head. Not just to the forehead—you must go clear to the top of the head.

Do this several times. Feel relaxation coming over your body. Each time you move up your body, you will feel more and more muscles relaxing.

If you have a hard time making the muscles relax in particular areas, tighten them up; then you will know which ones have to relax.

Take, for instance, the arm. Make a muscle and then relax. Tensing helps you to find a way to relax. Do this several times.

CHAPTER 6

Breath: The Vehicle
That Integrates Body and Mind

Everyone thinks he or she is breathing properly; but I insist that nearly every man and woman I meet is an improper breather.

Many programs today tell you to breathe deeply, low down in the diaphragm area. If you happen to be a student of the esoteric sciences learning meditation, you may be told to breathe deeply a few times or even to breathe deeply throughout the entire exercise.

Well, in this day and age everyone talks about going back to nature. That's exactly what we are going to do. We are going to go back to the proper way of breathing.

Once again, lie on the floor. Breathe from your diaphragm. See your stomach come out where the diaphragm is.

Make it come out. This is important.

Now fill your midsection of the lungs. Go up into the higher chest and lung region. As you do, you will feel the diaphragm push up and air move into the lung sacs. This is complete breathing. This is the natural method of breathing.

As you breathe, do not make jerky movements. You must breathe very smoothly. Make it come naturally.

After you have inhaled, retain the breath for a few seconds, then exhale quite slowly, holding the chest in a firm position, drawing the abdomen in a bit and lifting it up slowly as the air leaves the lungs. When the air is entirely exhaled, relax the chest and abdomen.

A little practice will render this part of the exercise easy, and the movement, once acquired, will be afterward performed almost automatically.

The yogi bases his rhythmic breathing time upon a unit which corresponds to the beat of his heart. Although the heartbeat varies in different persons, the heartbeat unit of each person provides his proper rhythmic breathing standard.

Ascertain your normal heartbeat by placing your fingers over your pulse, then counting one, two, three, four, five, six; one, two, three, four, five, six, etc., until the rhythm becomes firmly fixed in your mind.

With a little practice, you will be able to fix the rhythm so that you will be able to reproduce it easily. The beginner usually inhales about six pulse units, but he will be able greatly to increase this with practice.

The yogic rule for rhythmic breathing is that the units of inhalation and exhalation should be the same, while the units for retention between breaths should be one-half the number of those of inhalation and exhalation.

1. Sit erect in an easy posture, making certain to hold the chest, neck, and head as nearly in a straight line as possible, with shoulders slightly thrown back and hands resting easily on the lap.

In this position the weight of the body is largely supported by the ribs, and the position may be easily maintained. Yogis have found that one cannot get the best effect of rhythmic breathing with the chest drawn in and the abdomen protruding.

2. Inhale a complete breath slowly, counting six pulse units.

3. Retain, counting three pulse units.

4. Exhale slowly through the nostrils, counting six pulse units.

5. Count three pulse beats between breaths.

6. Repeat a number of times, but avoid fatiguing yourself at the start.

After a little practice you will be able to increase the duration of the inhalations and exhalations until about fifteen pulse units are consumed. As you increase, remember that the units for retention and between breaths is one-half the units of inhalation or exhalation. If you get up to fifteen, then hold for seven or eight.

Once you have mastered the Yoga rhythmic breathing, then you are well into the next step, which is concentration.

As you progress from one step to the next, remember that you must still go back and do the other steps each day, as well. Now that you are breathing properly, you do not stop exercising or learning to relax; nor do you stop having that ego, that little magic of believing in yourself. You must continue to work on all of them each day.

Why do I place so much importance on breathing? There are perhaps several reasons.

The cells of your body depend upon oxygen for life. When the oxygen supply is poor or circulation is decreased, the cells begin to die. The more oxygen that gets to all the cells and tissues of the body, the more the body will respond by regeneration instead of degeneration. The most efficient way to increase oxygen through increased circulation is through exercise, for breath is the vehicle that integrates body and mind.

When the brain is deprived of oxygen, the results are familiar—odd behavior, hallucinations, bad coordination, sometimes even death. The system of proper breathing can prevent many minor illnesses, such as headaches, indigestion, insomnia, and even some major illnesses, such as high blood pressure and heart attacks.

Even though there are various methods of breathing, the Yoga breathing technique is recognized as one of the best.

Researchers recently discovered only one major difference between the brain of a genius and that of an average man. There is a better blood and oxygen circulation to the brain of a genius.

CHAPTER 7

Focusing the Mind

The next step toward self-mastery and the elimination of pain is concentration.

Here is an exercise in concentration which involves focusing the mind on the flame of a candle.

Select a time when you have no food in your stomach (wait until at least two hours after you have eaten). It seems somehow that the digestive process interferes with the ability to relax and to meditate.

Place a lighted candle on a table a few feet in front of you. Then, sitting in a comfortable position, close your eyes and go through the process of relaxing the muscles from the toes up to the head in order to get your body in a very relaxed position.

After you are quite relaxed and doing your rhythmic breathing at the same time, continue to become very comfortable, very relaxed. Let everything go from your mind.

Now, still breathing deeply in a very relaxed position, open your eyes and concentrate on the flickering candle flame that you placed a few feet in front of you.

Concentrate on that flame.

Become a part of the flame.

Permit nothing else in the world to exist but that flame.

At this point, you must block out any traffic sounds, anything that exists around you. Nothing can exist at this point but the candle flame.

Think of nothing but the candle flame for perhaps twenty minutes.

I do not believe that the various exercises and techniques should last longer than twenty minutes, because after that time, one will begin to force.

As you learn and as you develop and as you grow, it will all become easier. You may practice as long as you like; but when you are beginning, practice very gently and very easily. Let things flow freely.

Another method that I use for developing concentration is to look at one's image in a mirror.

I use a mirror so that when I sit I can see myself from chest to head—a bust image of myself. On each side of the mirror I set a candle and sit perhaps two or three feet away from the mirror.

The candles should be sitting on both sides of the mirror so that you cannot see the image of the candle in the mirror.

Gaze intently into your eyes after, of course, you've gone through the relaxation process and rhythmic breathing. Focus upon your eyes, and just keep concentrating so that nothing exists but the image of you in the mirror.

As you sit looking and developing concentration, you can begin to program yourself, as well. Whenever you're in pain of any kind, you can begin to replace the sensation of that pain with thought.

The mind is very complex, but it is very simple, too. It can only accept one sensation at a time. Thought is a sensation, and pain is also a sensation. Theoretically, by out-thinking pain, you have none.

As you fill your mind with the image of the flame (or your own image in the mirror), pain will begin to leave the body. You should not think about the pain, even though you are aware of its existence.

Once you get to the point of concentration, you can withdraw the pain, because your body has already reached a very relaxed state. You have developed a certain degree of concentration. You have permitted your thoughts to replace the pain.

CHAPTER 8

A True State of Meditation

Most of the people who use the word "meditation" are talking about concentration, and sometimes vice-versa. The two words are used so synonymously in our culture that I feel it is about time we achieve a true perspective and put each in its proper place.

There is an active state of meditation, and there is a passive state of meditation. The active state of meditation should be an interim state between concentration and meditation, and we should call it contemplation.

In this active state of meditation, when one has concentrated his efforts on one subject, one thought, and entered a very relaxed state, he will begin contemplating and he will begin to receive answers.

The true state of meditation comes after the mind has focused on one particular thing until it has released its hold on the subject of focus and has become open, blank, receptive. At this point, one is in tune with the universe, the superconscious, or God—call it whatever you like.

It seems as though there is an electric charge going through you. You enter a state of bliss. You are in tune with everything. You are one with everything.

This is the state of true achievement; and very, very few people who claim to be meditating have ever reached this state. But once you have, it is so blissful, so wondrous, that it is literally beyond words.

This is the state to which one in meditation aspires. But it is in the contemplative states where you begin to program yourself so that the various ills and pains which afflict you will cease to exist.

When someone says, "Meditate on something," that is incorrect. One does not meditate on something, he *concentrates* on something.

When you meditate, you come into tune with the godhead or the superconscious mind or the higher self.

When one reaches a true state of meditation, he loves every man. He loves the world. He loves everything in it; and, of course, he loves himself. This is a true love of the spiritual self.

CHAPTER 9

How to Practice Pain Control

By following the exercises which I have described in the previous chapters, and by utilizing the various techniques and methods which I shall soon outline, I have been able to keep pain a virtual stranger in my life. I have been hospitalized on only one occasion—when I developed a cyst on the tailbone, which grew to be as large as a grapefruit. When I finally had it operated on, I was told that I would have to be in the hospital for a week.

On Monday I had the operation; on Wednesday morning I was released.

I had had an operation, but I had absolutely no

subsequent pain from it. There was pressure, of course; but there was no discomfort because my mind would not allow the pain to function.

A few years later I developed a kidney stone caused by a childhood problem. I decided to go to a doctor to see if my own diagnosis of a kidney stone was correct, and to see if my analysis of the severe pain in the abdominal region was accurate.

In the three days before I could find time to go to the doctor, I learned how to end even that severe pain.

I did go to the doctor, however, to be certain that it wasn't actually appendicitis, or something like that. When I told the doctor what the symptoms were, he poked around a bit, took an X ray to substantiate his conclusions, then stated that he agreed with my diagnosis. I subsequently passed the kidney stone with no pain.

Six months later another kidney stone developed. There was the onset of pain again, but I very quickly got rid of it.

I have been told by those who have suffered from such affliction that there is nothing more severe than the pain of a kidney stone. But, again, I passed it with no pain.

Another six months passed and I again received the pain that told me another kidney stone was forming. That's when I vowed I had had enough of such nonsense!

The doctor informed me that once the body begins to build up kidney stones, it will probably do so all of one's life. At this point in medical research, there does not seem to be any diet or any particular medication that will help eliminate the build-up of kidney stones. But since I decided that I would not have kidney stones anymore—and that's been ten years ago—I have never had a recurrence since. Nor have I ever had any symptoms that another kidney stone might be building up.

When people ask me if I am on a special diet, or if I observe a special diet, I answer: "Yes, anything that tastes good!"

That is basically what my diet is. I love vegetables; I love rare steaks. I love many foods. In fact, there are very few foods that I've ever eaten that I do not like.

But the biggest problem with most American people—and people in other parts of the civilized world, as well—is that they eat too much and too often. Here in the United States, we eat because it has been dictated and programmed to us. When we get up in the morning, we eat breakfast; at twelve o'clock noon, we eat lunch; at five or six or seven o'clock in the evening, we eat dinner. We eat whether we need it or not.

The American people are notorious for eating too much. Throughout most of my growing and maturing years, I ate only one meal a day. That is true even today. Occasionally, I eat a light snack at some other time of the day. One should eat and do everything in moderation.

I also maintain that most people sleep too much. If you sleep more than seven and one-half hours a night, you are sleeping too much, in my opinion. I sleep three or four hours a night, and I've done this since I was a teenager.

I found out that when I sleep this particular regimen, I am much more energetic. I am much more alert.

In my own research, I have found that people who sleep six hours or less a night are the most energetic, the most alert, the most active. People who sleep more than six hours—in the category of eight or more—seem to be slow, sluggish, and not as effective as producers.

Again, I concede this could be a psychological factor relating to their unhappiness with life. They may, in effect, be trying to sleep their lives away!

On November 25, 1975, I received a letter from Thomas B. in Connecticut. Thomas told me that he had been following my step-by-step method to self-mastery of pain control to find help in his emotional problems. The man had suffered his first nervous breakdown twenty years before and had had subsequent seizures ever since, resulting in three breakdowns all together. He complained that before he tried self-mastery he had never been emotionally healthy.

"I have faithfully followed your directions," Thomas told me. "At the present time, I am able to take naps for a few minutes and wake up completely refreshed. Sunday I watched two football games on television, and my eyes became tired. I followed your directions. Within ten minutes my eyes were refreshed. I can't tell you how much your directions have helped me in other ways. I hope that I have been able to give you an idea of how your techniques have helped."

Recently I received a telephone call from a schoolteacher in West Virginia who said that my methods had at last put the man's health matters into a proper perspective, the way things should be, and that he was getting tremendous results from using my techniques.

A lady in Canton, Ohio, who suffered migraine headaches, attended my classes and reported that she began receiving almost immediate relief.

I do not personally heal people. I can only describe

my techniques of pain control. I can only describe what I have done to unite my own mind and body and what others should be able to do.

I am neither a holy man nor a superman, but one who has learned simple techniques for circumventing pain.

I believe that the step-by-step method toward self-mastery that I outlined in the previous section can give anyone complete control over himself or herself, both mentally and physically. Once one gains such mind and body control, it is not difficult to eliminate a particular pain, ache, discomfort, tension, or ailment. Even some cases of cancer have been cured by using the mind.

I have not gleaned this information from books, but from the basic essences which I have isolated by working with human life. Throughout my lifetime I have been exposed to many people, and I have studied them. I have seen the aches, miseries, and pains of men and women. I have understood that what everyone is trying to do is to master the ultimate step where body and mind will be aligned. It is through this union that pain control is achieved.

Permit me to share with you the account of a most remarkable woman named Evelyn Monahan and how she learned to control pain and a variety of physical disabilities.

In 1961, at the age of twenty-two, Evelyn Monahan began to experience severe mental and physical afflictions resulting from various accidents.

One of these accidents involved a severe blow to the back of her head, causing her to become almost totally blind.

Then, a few months later, she was besieged by epileptic seizures resulting from the same head injury.

She was told that the damage to her nervous system was beyond repair and that her afflictions would be permanent.

As if these tragic instances were not enough, Ms. Monahan contracted an allergy in 1968 which caused an abcess to form upon her neck.

Her doctor, while making an incision to drain the abcess, accidentally severed one of the cranial nerves in her neck. This resulted in permanent paralysis of Ms. Monahan's right arm and shoulder.

Understandably, Evelyn Monahan became filled with hostility and resentment toward the world. She was blind, partially paralyzed, given to epileptic seizures, and had suffered severe mental and emotional trauma.

Today, however, Evelyn is not blind, nor does she experience epileptic seizures. Today, Evelyn enjoys the full use of all her limbs. She directs her own nonprofit research foundation and is a college teacher. She is active in sports, is a published author, and a lecturer in demand all over the country.

How was Evelyn Monahan able to overcome such overwhelming physical and emotional handicaps to literally accomplish the impossible?

She insists that what she refers to as extended sensory perception was largely responsible for her return to health.

Ms. Monahan was reared a Roman Catholic and educated in the Catholic school system. After graduating from high school, she spent two years in a convent. The spiritual experience still plays a large part in her life, although she has become eclectic in her approach to religion.

The reality of a supreme being, as she experienced it, was a central ingredient in the repair of her physical body. She acknowledges this fact, and makes no attempt to apologize for her belief. She decided to employ the positive force of faith and believed she could, and would, be healed; that her faith would "save" her.

This potential of mind over matter was intriguing to the young woman. She and two of her friends evolved an idea through which they hoped Evelyn might be healed.

The basic idea was a simple one.

The three friends formed a "psychic battery." Their plan was to establish an around-the-clock focus of energy which was to be directed into Evelyn's body. This healing energy was to be in the form of white light which would enter her body and actually change the molecular structure of the brain. The three used a visualization technique wherein they actually "saw" the restoration of the tissues and cells occurring in their minds' eye.

They catalyzed this process with the application of pure faith that it was in fact working at every moment of the treatment. When one went off the "healing shift," another took it up and continued until she was relieved.

Throughout this experiment, Evelyn Monahan had complete faith that God would restore her to good health.

Eventually, her sight returned. Then the epileptic seizures ceased, and control returned to all her physical faculties. The healing technique which restored Evelyn's sight took a mere five days.

The Monahan miracle became fact. Evelyn Monahan believes this miracle technique is part of a universal principle and can be used by anyone who develops the mental and spiritual muscles to make it work.

Evelyn Monahan is a scientist. She makes it a point to document her work and experiences because she knows this is part of the scientific method.

Although her physical and mental abilities were impaired for years, she did graduate from college. She received a bachelor's degree in psychology and sociology from the University of Tennessee. She has a master's degree in education from Georgia State and has completed work in experimental psychology at Emory University. She completed her doctoral studies in educational psychology at Georgia State in Atlanta.

Besides this impressive formal education, Evelyn Monahan has been an avid student of parapsychology and psychical research.

One very significant development has grown out of the publicity and exposure of Evelyn Monahan's techniques.

Once, when she was on a radio program, the announcement was made that she was willing to work with the blind in some experiments in extended sensory perception. She made no promises that there would be sensational results, but only that she was willing to try. The result of this offer was a number of requests for assistance from handicapped people.

One young man, who was totally blind, came to her. After his training with Evelyn Monahan, this man has found a very interesting job. He is sorting engineering prints—by color! A blind man sorting prints by color has got to be an endorsement for extended sensory perception, and is a major breakthrough in the rehabilitation of the handicapped.

This same young man is also reported to have seen

his wedding pictures for the first time. He is still blind,
but he can describe what his wife looks like by touching
the photographs.

Evelyn Monahan is optimistic that in time these
techniques with the blind will have been perfected so
that they will be able to read without braille.

To continue these experiments, Evelyn Monahan
has founded the Psychic Science Institute (PSI) in
Atlanta. It is her hope to one day be able to devote
most of her time to this work with the handicapped.
Once she is able to support herself entirely by her
writing, lecturing, and teaching, she can afford to do
the volunteer work at the institute. She is intense in her
belief that there should be no charge for the services for
the Psychic Science Institute.

When asked to speculate about the potential for her
techniques of extended sensory perception as they
could apply to other forms of disabilities, Ms.
Monahan responded:

"I have come to believe the whole body is a sensing
mechanism. We have been given to accept the role of
the five senses performing in a limited, restricted way.
The eyes see, the ears hear, the nose smells, the skin
feels, the tongue tastes—*period*. Our experiments
indicate that the entire body—every inch of it—is a
sensing device.

"Our senses can be extended to feed visual or other
information to the brain. The psychic senses are really
the extended sensory perceptors of the individual
human organism. The deaf, for example, can benefit
tremendously from telepathy. We have done research
on this and have found that a message received
telepathically is received in the language of the
receiver, no matter in what language it is sent. All these

techniques for expanding the consciousness will help handicapped people to communicate with us and to understand things better.

"As for understanding psychic abilities in the rest of us, we have a long way to go. I was lucky to have grown up in a family where psychic ability was accepted. I think that a lot of kids get this squashed out of them.

"They may evidence a degree of telepathy, clairvoyance, precognitive dreams, or psychometry as a child. They are told by adults that this cannot be. They are told what their limitations are. Unfortunately, many children accept these explanations and suppress their experiences from then on.

"I think it would be far wiser to teach children their potential (including their psychic abilities) than to concentrate on their limitations."

In my first two steps toward self-mastery, you should learn to restructure your life toward a whole new area. You should make yourself emanate love, because you are learning what love is really all about.

A person who thinks very negative thoughts creates an imbalance of hormones in his glandular system; and this causes aches, pains, misery, colds, flu, sickness of all sorts. Man must restructure his life to become a positive, happy person in order to achieve the ultimate and to be able to control himself through the steps of self-mastery.

The Power of Positive Attitude

You can't say, "I wish" or "I would like to." It must be,

"I want; I will have." You must be very, very positive.
You must become so strongly positive that you feel it
within every fiber of the body.

Breathing

The complete breath and rhythmic breathing, as
outlined in a previous chapter, will bring you well
along on the proper road toward self-mastery.

I hope that I will not confuse you if I speak of *Prana,*
as the yogis do. When the yogis breathe, they say they
are breathing in *Prana,* the life-giving force.

Perhaps for our Western minds, if we substitute
electricity for Prana, we will get basically the same
idea.

As a man breathes in and does the Yoga breathing
exercises, he builds up a charge, a very strong electrical
charge, along the spine. The spine actually becomes
like a big capacitor.

As the charge builds up and a person wants to emit
energy, he is able to change his electromagnetic field,
causing him to heal himself.

In the instance of a healer, when he lays his hand
upon another, he is releasing the charge that's been
built up in his capacitor. Through the emission of
electrical impulses from his healing hands, he is able to
change the other person's electromagnetic field,
causing him, in essence, to heal himself through the
stimulus of the healer.

Relaxation

Relaxation emphasizes that you must tone the body, as well as the mind, and get them both into proper functioning order. It takes a very positive attitude to continue. It takes commitment; it takes discipline. But it is important to engage in exercise and to improve the circulation of the blood.

Concentration-Contemplation-Meditation

The active state of meditation, which I call contemplation, is comparable to the state of mind a person is in just before he falls asleep. If you want to eliminate aches and pains, it will be at this level of contemplation, or active meditation, that you will do it. It is at this point where you will begin to program yourself to the state where you will be able to get rid of pains and whatever else might be troubling you. *It is in this state of mind that you can visualize perfect health, happiness, vitality, and no pain!*

You can program into your superconscious a conviction that you are capable of doing whatever you wish—even to the point where you are able to conquer pain. Programming is essential, and I believe the contemplative state is the one in which to obtain this level of consciousness, just prior to advancing into the total, passive state of meditation.

But you must not confuse yourself. You must be very certain. You must analyze the cause of your pain. You must seek a doctor before you try to control a pain about which you know nothing.

A headache can be caused by a brain tumor, and I do not want anyone stifling a pain from a tumor when they should be seeking medical help!

There are so many ways that pain can strike. Pain does not have to affect the specific part of the body from which it seems to be emanating. The pain may be coming from somewhere totally different from where it seems.

Again, I repeat, *check with your medical doctor* before undergoing this, or any other program of pain control.

CHAPTER 10

*A Simple Five-Day
Pain-Control Program*

THE FIRST DAY

THE FIRST FIVE-MINUTE SESSION

Sit comfortably in a chair. Your back should be straight. Your legs should not be crossed; your feet should be flat on the floor.

As you breathe in, mentally state the words, "I feel . . ." As you breathe out, mentally state the words, ". . . no pain."

Your respiration should be natural and unforced as you repeat: "I feel . . . no pain. I feel . . . no pain."

This simple exercise is both a mental and a physical technique which relaxes the body, regulates respiration, and mentally conditions you to eliminate pain from your thinking processes. Continue this exercise for about three minutes.

Remain seated and proceed to the second technique in your first five-minute period of pain-control conditioning.

This exercise, the head roll, will loosen up the muscles, arteries, and veins of the neck and shoulders, all of which affect the ears, eyes, throat, and other organs of the body.

Sit up straight. Drop your head forward onto your chest. Without lifting the head, roll it to the left, up and over the left shoulder and over the back as far as possible.

After rolling your head to the left a few times, reverse and go the right. Make as many complete circles as possible. Repeat this exercise for approximately two minutes.

If you should begin to experience a slight dizziness, cease the exercise and finish the two-minute time period with repetitions of "I feel...no pain."

THE SECOND FIVE-MINUTE SESSION

Begin with two minutes of the head roll.

Conclude with three minutes of rhythmically breathing "I feel...no pain."

You have now begun and ended the first day of your program with the positive affirmation that you will not permit pain in your life.

Your very act of breathing—the physical action that most assures one of being alive—has aided you in making this declaration of independence from unnecessary pain.

THE SECOND DAY

THE FIRST FIVE-MINUTE SESSION

Stand up straight with your heels quite close together.
Raise up on your toes, hold for a count of three, then
lower yourself back down on your heels. This exercise
is a good overall toner for the legs.

If an injury should somehow prevent you from
performing the heel raise, sit up straight and flex your
calf and thigh muscles for a three-second count.

The heel raise should be performed for approximately one minute.

Follow the heel raise with about two minutes of
head rolls.

Complete your first five-minute session of the
second day with two minutes of rhythmically breathing, "I feel . . . no pain."

THE SECOND FIVE-MINUTE SESSION

Begin this session with a simple stretching exercise.
Stand erect, feet comfortably apart. Raise your arms
over your head and stretch for the ceiling.

Imagine your arms actually growing and reaching
the light fixture.

Visualize your palms flattening against the ceiling.

Even if an injury should prevent your standing
erect, you may remain seated and still reach for the
ceiling.

When tension in your arms becomes uncomfortable, lower them for a few seconds, then stretch once
again.

This simple stretching exercise will help remove
pressure against vertebrae which may be pressing

against certain nerves and causing pain. Continue this technique for two minutes.

Follow the stretching exercise with about one minute of head rolls to continue the relaxation of neck vertebrae.

Conclude this session with two minutes of rhythmically breathing, "I feel . . . no pain."

The Third Day

THE FIRST FIVE-MINUTE SESSION

Begin with one minute of stretching.

Follow with one minute of heel raises.

Conclude with one minute of head rolls, two minutes of rhythmically breathing, "I feel . . . no pain."

THE SECOND FIVE-MINUTE SESSION

Lie flat on the floor. For one minute, rhythmically breathe, "I feel . . . no pain." While continuing to breathe rhythmically, focus on the area of your body which is causing you pain.

Visualize the painful area as being colored a bright red. Imagine that you have a cool, damp cloth in your hand and begin to rub away the area of pain.

As the area becomes smaller and smaller, visualize the pain disintegrating, leaving you forever.

Conclude this session by rhythmically breathing, "I feel . . . no pain."

THE FOURTH DAY

THE FIRST FIVE-MINUTE SESSION

Begin this session by standing erect, raising your arms over your head, then bending at the waist to touch your toes. Do not despair if you cannot reach your toes. It is the effort and the stretching that is important.

If it is impossible to perform this exercise, either stand or sit erect and contract your stomach muscles as best you can for a count of three. Continue this exercise for one minute.

Rest for a moment, then proceed with one minute of stretching for the ceiling, one minute of head rolls.

Rest for a bit between those exercises and the concluding technique, which today is to perform one minute of heel raises closely followed by one minute of rhythmically breathing, "I feel... no pain."

THE SECOND FIVE-MINUTE SESSION

Stand before a mirror and concentrate on your face.

While rhythmically breathing, "I feel... no pain," permit your face to assume a happier and happier expression.

Visualize the pain leaving your body as your smile becomes wider and more reflective of good health. Continue for the full five-minute session.

THE FIFTH DAY

THE FIRST FIVE-MINUTE SESSION

Begin the session by standing erect before a chair. Bend your knees until your buttocks touch the seat of the chair. Do not drop lower, but raise to a standing position at once. Repeat knee bends for one minute.

Continue by touching your toes for one minute, stretching for the ceiling for one minute, doing head rolls for one minute.

Rest for only a moment, then conclude with heel raises. This time, however, mentally recite, "I feel..." as you lift upward on your toes, "...no pain," as you lower to your heels. Repeat for one minute.

THE SECOND FIVE-MINUTE SESSION

Stand before a mirror and mentally appraise yourself. Notice how much more relaxed your face appears. Take a moment to assess how much better your body feels. Pain is becoming a stranger to your life.

While still focusing on your smiling, healthy face, rhythmically breathe in forceful, joyful affirmation: "I feel... *no pain!* I feel... *no pain!*" Continue for the full five-minute session.

CHAPTER 11

Headaches

For simple headache, lie down on the floor and do the breathing exercises as described in previous chapters. This will relax the muscles in the head so that it will feel as though the skull suddenly opens up and permits the pain to go fleeting out of it.

The tension headache is caused by muscle contractions which result in a band-like pain at the base of the skull. This is usually caused by anxiety or fatigue.

There is the vascular headache which involves the arteries, both inside and outside of the skull. These are the throbbing pains that people feel. These are the migraine headaches.

Another type of headache would be an inflammatory headache associated with sinusitis, infected teeth, and numerous other things.

Perhaps yet a different kind of headache might be called a psychogenic headache, which may be caused by hormone deficiencies in the brain.

If one suffers from chronic headaches, then I must repeat that he should follow the steps toward self-mastery and reorder his life. He must recognize the source of tension, of the continual pressure, and remove it. He must learn to have a self-directed form of relaxation.

People must learn to live less stressful, more meaningful lives. They must find a purpose in life, even if it may be an interesting hobby. By focusing on some kind of activity, a lot of the stresses that cause headaches will be reduced.

I would also recommend that people drink plenty of water. The majority of people simply do not drink enough water to flush out the poisons from the body. These poisons may sometimes cause headaches.

A person should eat wisely and not too much. A well-balanced diet may also serve to eliminate many of the causes of chronic headaches.

I have been emphasizing the negative effects of mental, nervous, and physical fatigue, suggesting that the majority of headaches may come from tension and overwork. At the same time, some headaches are caused by too much leisure. A person who has nothing to do begins to think about his illnesses, thereby magnifying them.

Other men and women may have pent-up emotions which they have not released. If you should find yourself in such a situation, you should ventilate your emotions—even if it's talking to yourself in the mirror!

Air your feelings verbally. This will sometimes eradicate headaches.

Each person must strive to seek the real reason for his headache. Once he has determined the principle cause of his chronic headache, he must then practice moderation in eating, sleeping, drinking, etc., and he will become a much happier person, a much stronger individual. He will become much more mentally alert.

As I have pointed out, it is not necessary to do any strenuous exercises in order to tone up the body; but the main thing in eradicating any type of pain, whether headache or otherwise, is to get a good circulation going through the body.

Here is a good exercise in regard to eliminating the pain of a headache.

Sit in a chair, and do the relaxation exercise where you begin telling the muscles of your body that they are to relax. Start at the tip of your toes and go clear to the top of your head. This will relieve tension and stress and help you get things in order.

In a relaxed body, the heartbeat and respiration rate are slowed down. There is a deceleration in metabolism and a reduction in tension. Skin resistance is also increased. These things will help in the case of a headache.

In migraine headaches, some research has indicated that warming the hands actually helps alleviate the pain. Some people take warm baths to help them handle their migraines.

Here is a simple breathing exercise which will help to clear the head and eradicate any pain that may be persistent.

Sit with your spine straight. Relax the body and

bend slightly forward. Put your finger on the right nostril, inhale through the left nostril. Breathe in through the left nostril as deeply as possible until you have a complete breath, filling your lungs completely.

Hold the breath for a little bit, then exhale again through the left nostril, still closing the right nostril. While exhaling, imagine you are directing the flow of the breath up the spine into your brain, spreading it like a spray.

Do this about ten times. You will feel your head cooling down, and it will seem like a third of the air is coming out of your ears.

With a few days' conditioning, this exercise will relieve congestion in the case of a head cold.

People with hearing problems have used this breathing technique, and it has actually improved their sense of hearing.

CHAPTER 12

Backaches

In all matters of pain control, the individual who is desirous of eradicating the pain must really want to get rid of it. When we come to backaches, I have found so often that many men and women actually seem to cherish this particular pain because it may remove them from certain uncomfortable social or domestic situations.

If one actually desires to rid himself of his backache, I suggest that he follow the meditation and exercise procedures as outlined in the previous chapters. Once one develops self-mastery, he can control all pain.

The simplest thing to do to remedy backache and to get rid of the pain is to stretch.

Stand up straight and stretch as high as you can. This pulls the vertebrae back into position and keeps them from pressing on the nerve that is causing the pain.

With a backache that has been caused by lifting, we may be talking about a pulled muscle. In some cases, it would be essential to see a doctor to be certain you do not have a slipped disc.

Any type of an exercise that strengthens the abdominal muscles will help the back problem, because it will place the pull on the muscles in the back.

Here is an exercise that I have found beneficial in easing backache pain.

Lie flat on the floor and raise the legs gently until they are in a vertical position with the floor, then let them down very slowly. This works the abdominal region, as well, but it affects the lower back area especially.

This same exercise seems to help give more muscle to the back and to ease pinched nerves. I suggest that this be repeated ten times.

Again, moderation. Perhaps perform the exercise twice in the morning and again in the evening.

Another exercise I utilize is to lie flat on the floor with the arms resting sideways. Raise your legs until you have lifted your entire body to rest on your shoulder blades. Bring your legs up until they go over the head and touch the floor. Basically, the head will be between the knees.

With the arms still resting as before and your chin almost down into your chest area, take a few deep breaths until you are able to take twenty-five to fifty.

Practice this daily. This not only develops power in your abdominal region, it is also very beneficial to the regenerative organs.

A basic factor in correcting back problems is to develop good posture. Sit upright, and this will eliminate many of the problems in the lower back area.

Remember to follow the steps to self-mastery, to practice meditation, and to perform exercises that will help develop the abdominal region, as well as the back.

CHAPTER 13

Indigestion and Heartburn

Chronic indigestion and heartburn can be corrected by proper eating habits. In the meantime, as you are focusing upon what is actually troubling you, what is causing you to eat so fast and to have so many worries, you will want to try to eradicate pain through certain relaxation exercises.

Relax the muscles in the abdominal region. Assume a half-crouching position and twist your body from side to side.

The pressure of the gas is pressing mainly in the diaphragm area, where it is causing you difficulty in breathing.

Bend over and touch your toes with your hands; or bend over, at least, as far as you can.

When we speak of chronic stomach pains or chronic stomach cramps, we are working on an area where, basically, we have an imbalance in the glandular body due to improper thinking. Ductless glands are causing this. Seek the cause first, of course.

Chronic stomach pains indicate the need for a change. So many people are working at jobs that they should not be in, and this is causing them all kinds of pains and problems. Sometimes one should seek another job in order to be more relaxed, peaceful, and happy. The housewife, too, is often tense, uptight. Even a good walk around the block can be helpful.

Meditating for fifteen minutes in the morning and fifteen minutes in the evening would change one's whole routine for the day, and lessen the impulse to rush through the workday.

Indigestion and heartburn are most often caused because a person is upset. Once one has gained a positive mental attitude and learned to believe in himself, then there is very little chance of his getting indigestion.

Here is another exercise that is good for relieving both indigestion and heartburn.

Sit or stand in an upright position with the body relaxed. Inhale deeply through the left nostril while holding the right nostril closed.

After taking a complete breath, hold both nostrils closed. Moisten the lips with your tongue and pucker up, as if you were going to be kissed.

Now begin to blow the breath through your lips while creating an "eeee" sound. As you are exhaling, pull the abdomen up with a strong effort.

Repeat this two or three times until you have your stomach pains under control.

CHAPTER 14

Muscle Sprains, Toothache, Stiff and Sore Muscles, Burns

Once you have gained self-mastery, you will be able to use the mind to eradicate pain whenever any of the above afflict you. But for temporary relief, here is an exercise that I have often used.

Sit comfortably in a chair in front of a table with a candle burning a few feet in front of you. Concentrate on the flame for a few minutes. Do deep breathing, at least, if not the total complete breath. I prefer the total complete breath, but some people find it difficult to achieve this quickly.

After a few moments, close your eyes and visualize that candle between your eyes. Feel the pains that are troubling you being drawn to the candle. Then visualize the candle leaving your body and going upward, ever upward. The pain is going, along with the candle flame.

Another method of trying to eradicate pain—let us take burns, for instance—is to relax immediately the burned area and make the mind think of it as being cooled down. This will not only take away the pain of the burn but, depending on how well-developed you have become mentally, cause the burned area not to blister.

In the case of bruises, relax the area where the bruise has occurred. You have torn blood vessels in that area, so it would seem natural that you would want to stop the flow of blood. But it should be the opposite. You should relax the area as much as possible and try mentally to get the blood flowing more strongly into that area. I believe that flushing out the area with blood will help alleviate the pain and encourage rapid healing.

CHAPTER 15

Aches and Pains from Tension

Energy is needed at this point as much as anything else. Keeping the mind free through meditation will provide additional energy.

An exercise would be to lace the fingers and place the interlocked hands on the back of the head. Pull forward with the hands, while pressing backward with the head. This would relieve tension of the neck muscles, which may be the cause of headache.

Tensions often beset you for very good reasons, primarily to prompt you to solve a problem at hand. But excess tension may cause great damage to your heart and your psyche, especially if the tensions arise over unimportant, harmless things.

If your anxieties are giving you sleepless nights, making you paranoid, or robbing you of the pleasures of life, here are some useful tips in dealing with excessive tension:

1. TALK OUT YOUR WORRIES. Confide your problem to some level-headed person. Another "eye" is often very useful in giving you a wider perspective. Just be certain that you have chosen a positive, not a negative, person in whom to confide.

2. ESCAPE FOR A WHILE. Go to a movie, read a book, take a short holiday, go off to the countryside. Just remember that these are only temporary escapes. You must return to the situation prepared to deal with the difficulty, but you should now be better composed. In certain instances, such as the death of a loved one, it might be better to become lost in a crowd, rather than to retreat somewhere alone.

3. WORK OFF YOUR ANGER. If you feel like slapping someone in the mouth, don't. Take that violent emotion and release it in some physical activity that requires a great deal of exertion. I, personally, have always found a great release in gardening, and I recommend it highly.

4. GIVE IN ONCE IN A WHILE. Stand your ground when you know that you are in the right, but be open-minded enough to make allowances for the fact that you might be wrong. And on occasion, if you are dead-right, it's easier on your system to make an intelligent compromise.

5. DO SOMETHING FOR OTHERS. This is an ancient, tried and true metaphysical remedy for taking the steam out of your own worries and for giving you a fine feeling of having done well.

6. TAKE ONE THING AT A TIME. When the workload piles up to the point where it seems unbearable, it is best to assess the situation and decide which of the tasks are the more urgent. Then pitch into them, one at a time, setting aside all the rest. Once the "biggies" have been disposed of, you will be able to ascertain that the remainder aren't really so bad after all.

7. AVOID THE SUPERMAN OR SUPERWOMAN SYNDROME. No one can be perfect in everything. No one can be liked by everybody. Stop trying to leap tall buildings in a single bound. Settle for the third or fourth stories. Decide which things in life you do really well, then put your energies and your major efforts into these areas.

8. TAKE IT EASY ON YOURSELF. Each of us has his own virtues, his own shortcomings, his own values, and his own right to develop as an individual. Take it a little easier on yourself and on others. Instead of always finding fault with those around you—and mercilessly nit-picking your own weaknesses—search out the good points in your own behavior and in the habits of those with whom you are in contact. Give yourself—and others—an opportunity to develop in a positive manner.

9. GIVE THE OTHER GUY AN EVEN BREAK. Modern society too often emphasizes the competitive element

in everything from sports to arithmetic assignments. Competition should be the seasoning that makes the meal more palatable. An overdose, though, can drive everyone from the table to gulp down water, just as an overdose of competition can drive one to a heart attack or a nervous breakdown. Cooperation can be as contagious as competition. When you give the other guy an even break, you can make things easier on yourself. He will no longer regard you as a threat and he will cease being a threat to you.

10. MAKE YOURSELF AVAILABLE. Instead of drawing away from others, make yourself available to them. Instead of always waiting to be asked, go ahead and make some of the overtures for a change.

11. SCHEDULE YOUR RECREATION. I shall always emphasize the importance of physical recreation. Exercise performed in a sensible manner, structured to your individual health quotient, is essential to proper physical and mental health. Set a routine and follow it. Make it a part of your daily regimen, rather than setting it apart.

12. EXPRESS YOUR SENSE OF HUMOR. Laughter is always an effective medicine. When pressure mounts, attempt to deflate it with a bit of "gallows humor." Try to see the humor in situations of crisis. Laughter is contagious and tends to bind men and women together in a greater sense of comradeship. Also it helps to lessen the blow of life's many disappointments. One should not, of course, laugh at tasteless situations. Remember: the humor should come from the situation, not from the personalities of those involved;

therefore, one must always be careful to assess precisely at *what* he is about to laugh.

CHAPTER 16

Dull Pain and Fatigue

There are two kinds of fatigue. One is due to toxins and poisons accumulating in the body. The other results from the negative attitude of the mind.

The mind is a reservoir of energy. If you want to have positive energy all the time, then you must maintain a positive mental attitude.

Fatigue can easily be eradicated by right breathing and by drinking plenty of water. Eight glasses a day is a good minimum.

I sometimes will drink as many as three gallons of water or other types of liquid a day. I do not retain the water in my body, a fact which I attribute to the type of conditioning which I have given my mind throughout the years.

Here is a method used by yogis which I have successfully employed to help rid the body of fatigue.

Basically, what this breathing exercise does is to charge the solar plexus. Take the breath by quick sniffs until you feel a cool feeling in your solar-plexus area.

Then sniff faster until it gets hot in that same area.

Sniff even faster...faster...faster—until your head feels a power running through it that almost makes you dizzy.

Then you sniff still faster until you feel a strong stimulation. Increase the rate of breathing until you feel a strong pain around the neck muscles. Then you should stop.

Proceed gradually in this breath exercise. Within a week you should be bubbling over with energy.

This is an excellent manner in which to invigorate yourself and to eliminate fatigue. Breathing, right attitude, toning of the mind and body, all blend together.

CHAPTER 17

Eye Strain

Eye strain, of course, causes headaches, so by relieving eye strain you might relieve the headache that is bothering you.

One particular method I have found useful in relieving eye strain is to take a pencil and hold it about a foot in front of the face.

Focus your eyes on the pencil for a few minutes, then look beyond the pencil into a distance for a minute or so. Then look back at the pencil, focusing your eyes both times intently on the distance and close-up, distance and close-up.

Do this for about five minutes, looking at the pencil, roughly, say, for a few seconds, focusing the eyes upon it, then on the distance, then on the pencil, back and forth, etc.

There is another exercise that could be used to strengthen the eyes and to relieve pressure as well.

Stand in an upright position, your feet about two feet apart. Put one of your fingers on the right nostril, inhale deeply through the left nostril, until your chest fully expands and you have your lungs completely filled.

Then hold both nostrils and focus your attention on the area between the eyebrows. Keep your attention focused there. Pretend there is a little ball there between the eyebrows, and you are gazing at it. While you are doing this, think very, very positive thoughts; because what you meditate on, or what you think, you will become.

Still clamping the nostrils closed, and holding your breath and meditating on good thoughts, bend your head and knees and lower yourself as low as possible until you feel a strong pulsation of blood to the top of your head. You will feel the blood surging to your eyes. Your face will feel flushed. Your tongue will swell with blood and seem almost to fill the entire cavity of your mouth.

When those four conditions have been realized, slowly raise up and let the breath escape from the opposite nostril. (You breathed in through the *left* nostril; now hold the left nostril and breathe out through the *right* nostril.)

When you have completely straightened your body, breathe out.

Many people feel a little dizzy, but this is mainly

because the brain cells have become congested. If you practice this exercise diligently, in about three days the dizziness will not bother you anymore.

CHAPTER 18

Arthritis and Rheumatism

In addition to easing pain of arthritis and rheumatism, this exercise gives a little boost to the kidneys and stimulates the lymphatic system and the liver.

Stand with your heels together. Inhale deeply and fully, then hold your breath.

While holding your breath, turn your head to the right until your neck muscles are pulled as taut as possible. This must be done without moving the body. Stretch until you cannot turn any further, then hold to the point of dizziness. (It may be advisable to lean on a chair for balance at this point.) Now exhale through the mouth.

Repeat this process three times on the right side, then three times on the left side. Each time try to hold the taut muscles just a little bit longer.

This exercise will help arthritis and rheumatism because it stimulates the adrenal glands and encourages them to produce more natural cortisone.

CHAPTER 19

Accidents

Place yourself in a state of mind so that you can relax the injured muscles.

Be careful, however, because if you are unsure of the extent of the injury, you do not want to cause further damage.

The less you do in such a case, especially if it is severe, the better.

Suffer the pain until the doctor diagnoses what has actually happened. In some instances it is necessary to feel pain, so that when the doctor does inquire where it hurts, you can tell him explicitly.

Try to relax as much as possible. Cover the body to keep the muscles warm and relaxed.

Rhythmic breathing can give you a focal point of concentration which will help ease the pain until your injuries can be examined by a doctor.

CHAPTER 20

Discomfort of the Common Cold

With my self-mastery plan, you will not have colds! But until you have achieved total self-mastery, proper breathing—the complete breathing and the rhythmic breathing program, along with meditation will be beneficial.

With proper lung ventilation, you will not get colds. I have not had a cold in over twenty-five years! I attribute that enviable record to my breathing program.

Breathing, meditation, and rest—rather than the much advised "two aspirins"—comprise my remedy for quick recovery from the common cold.

Nearly everything that man wants and is looking for lies within himself, but man must continually feed the brain so that he has the conscious support and the complete confidence of the brain's ability to eradicate pain from the body. Through the program I have outlined, you can learn how to control pain. You will be able to eliminate headaches and some of the other ailments before they ever begin.

When you gain peace of mind, when you become a happy individual, you will never suffer again. Once you have reached the blissful state of active meditation, pain will cease to exist for you.

CHAPTER 21

*Programming the Child
for Pain Control*

It has often been said by many who have observed and
studied man that when we are first born into this world
we possess almost god-like abilities.

Through our early programming, however, many of
these qualities are "educated" out of us by parents,
friends, teachers, and society in general.

Such "deprogramming" leaves us less than complete, and our lives become very stressful. We are left
with many pent-up emotions, which help to cause our
many aches, pains, and sicknesses.

When we as children are pushed out into the
world—much as birds force their nestlings to fly and to

fend for themselves—we suddenly come to the realization that there is much more to man than we had been led to believe.

If we are sensitive men and women, we may spend the rest of our lives attempting to gain back some of the god-like qualities with which we were born.

Regretfully, too many people never regain these abilities, but endure lives of frustration filled with yearning and earnest searching.

Others are able to see glimpses of the greater reality, but they are never able to achieve a complete return.

Even though pain and misery, which surround each of us, can be compensated for by taking "two aspirins" or by investing long hours in doctors' offices and hospitals endeavoring to bring ourselves back into balance, those of us who are sensitive or those of us who suffer chronic pain soon realize that these stopgap measures are not the true answers. Even the exercises and techniques delineated by me in Chapters Ten through Twenty are only transient answers designed to enable one to persevere so that he or she might find the true answer in self-mastery.

As parents we owe it to ourselves and, more importantly, to our children to start teaching them a new way of life—a life whereby, using their own energies, they may be able to overcome pain and illness.

It is most important that such a program begin when the child is young—even when he or she is still in the cradle. We must be able to guide our children and to help them retain those god-like qualities with which they were born, so that their lives can be ones of their own making. And most importantly, so their lives may be happy ones.

Too often when I am around parents and their children, I hear the adults negatively programming their offspring, magnifying their hurts, adversely affecting their development.

For instance, when a child falls down and "hurts" himself, the overly protective parent immediately runs to him and says soothingly, "Are you hurt? Can Mama (or Daddy) help?"

At this point the child begins to weep and howl in exaggerated pain. And the next time he or she bumps into a table edge or falls off a tricycle, the process of noisy grief will be repeated in order to bring the parent to soothe the injury.

The native intelligence of the child causes him to recognize the fact that a sure method of receiving the attention he needs is to inform the parent that he is "hurt." It is unfortunate that that is the only way in which some children receive adequate attention from their too busy and neglectful parents.

As the years go by, the child's hurts become more and more magnified because he has learned how to receive regularly the attention which is otherwise denied him. The pattern has become solidified. Throughout his or her adult years, he will always complain of one misery after another. His spouse, his employer, his friends will grow weary of forever hearing these tales of woe.

It is so strange. By rushing to her child's side at his first whimper, the mother thought that she was doing such a good thing. She will probably never realize that she did her child more harm than good by being overly solicitous.

I am not advocating that a parent should ignore his or her child's needs when the little one truly injures himself, but I am urging every mother and father to place these hurts and bumps in a proper perspective. Do not overbalance.

How should one go about programming a child in the proper direction?

First, we must realize that each child is an individual personality and that each one will require different attentions.

In many cases, if we really take the time to know a child, he will help direct us in the correct manner to provide the right things he needs in his life as he needs them.

From earliest infancy, one should display warmth and love to his child. But this parental loving should never extend to the point of over-coddling the child or of being overly protective.

Once love and warmth have been established in the child's psyche, we can proceed as parents with the knowledge that we have established a contact which informs the child that he is being fully accepted into its environment.

As we continue to listen to the child and to learn its real needs, we may utilize this information to begin forming the child's personality or ego and start the child on a program which will build positive mental attitudes.

We must be very careful not to make the child become egotistical or confused in his thinking.

Egoism is healthy, but egotism will become negative and will seriously affect any future programming.

I must re-emphasize the point that there is a close relationship between ego and positive mental attitude. They go hand in hand in personality development.

It should also be repeated that a little negativity is

not undesirable, for it can make life more interesting.

As the child begins to mature and begins to advance in the early stages of education, he should be taught the remaining program as outlined in the steps to self-mastery described in Chapters Two to Eight.

The first twelve years are highly important in the development of a child. During this period he must have exercises which will strengthen the heart muscles and all the veins and arteries which lead to that vitally important "pumping machine." Swimming and strenuous sports which help build the large muscle groups are of tremendous benefit to the maturing child. These activities should always be augmented with a regimen of some type of calisthenics for creating fine muscle tone.

The earlier you get your child into the development of concentration and meditation, the greater good will accrue for him or her.

As the child makes the transition into meditation, he will suddenly find himself being assisted in his development through his own intuitive mind.

When this begins to occur, it will become necessary for us to start to withdraw from a role of close supervision of his education in this area. It is not time for your nestling to leave the nest, take to wing, and fly solo.

Here is a suggested program for assisting your child to overcome pain and achieve control and self-mastery:

One to two years old: Instill love and warmth to build personality and ego. Emphasize a positive mental attitude.

Three to five years old: Initiate physical education programs. Continue ego-building and the development of a positive mental attitude. Teach proper breathing techniques.

Six to eight years old: Continue all other programs. Teach techniques of concentration.

Nine to ten years old: Continue all other programs. Make the transition from concentration to meditation.

Eleven throughout life: Seek after knowledge and wisdom. Maintain regular meditation. Continue a daily exercise regimen.

CHAPTER 22

Sharing the God Force

Healing is certainly one of the most beautiful acts of sharing which can occur between human beings, and I have always held the utmost respect for those men and women who have devoted their life energies to the healing arts.

At the same time, I have often pondered just what healing really is. Is it truly an energy force which can be channeled . . . or is it largely a matter of faith in the healer's ability to serve as an agent of the God force?

As the result of a series of experiments which he had been conducting since the 1950's, Dr. Bernard Grad, an associate professor in the department of psychiatry,

McGill University, Montreal, believes that the laying on of hands channels an actual healing force. In his opinion, the religious rite of laying on of hands releases a force or energy that can be measured under laboratory conditions. In addition, he is convinced that an "unseen energy or vital force" is released in all forms of human contact, from a kiss to the shaking of hands.

Dr. Grad attests to different qualities of healing energy, and he states: "A personal element of the healer may go along with this power, and if he himself or she is not moved by true selflessness and concern for others, the results could be negative. The healer must be concerned about his own spiritual state and live a moral life."

Although some of the claims which Cleve Backster, the polygraph expert, has made regarding plant communication are controversial, the series of experiments is relevant to a discussion of healing because they imply that all life is *one,* that there is a signal linkage which exists among all living things, that there is unity to all creation. Such a belief is basic to the essential philosophies of all the great metaphysicians of history.

In his *Blueprint for Immortality,* Dr. Harold Saxton Burr hypothesizes that humans, animals, and vegetables have distinctive electrical field patterns. If there exists such a universal electrodynamic field phenomenon that flows through every living thing, then our science may one day fully accredit the ancient custom of laying on of hands through the instrumentation of its own technology.

Dr. Paul E. Morentz, chief of the psychiatric service of a Veterans Administration Hospital in California, has pointed out that faith healing preceded the medical profession by many centuries.

"Our advances in modern medicine often make us forget that the body has enormous powers to heal itself if these can be brought to bear on the illness," Dr. Morentz said. "It is imperative that we keep an open and inquiring mind about the whole phenomenon of healing."

Recently, the conservative journal *Medical Economics* carried an article about Olga Worrall entitled "Even M.D.'s Have Faith in This Faith Healer."

According to Mrs. Worrall: "I simply channel to the afflicted man or woman a primal healing power that flows from God. So-called miracles are the working out of the laws of God. I have no bag of tricks—no mumbo-jumbo. Faith healing is a technique that goes back to Biblical times, and we have plenty of evidence that it works. Most religions still believe in it, but few still practice it—which is a pity."

Every Thursday morning for the past twenty-six years, hundreds of sick people have filled a Baltimore church to receive spiritual healing. And at precisely nine o'clock every night these same people, along with thousands of others who suffer from physical, mental, and spiritual ailments, pause for five minutes to give and receive the healing energy which is purported to flow into them from God through the hands of a gifted healer.

Are these people desperately chasing rainbows, or is there indeed something tangible to be found in spiritual healing?

Ambrose and Olga Worrall established an untarnished record as spiritual healers of astonishing ability. They worked privately to aid the sick and participated in countless miracles during that time.

The Worralls concentrated much of their healing on sick children. Children with twisted limbs, diseased organs, and hopeless prognoses came to the Worralls for assistance and relief. So did adults from all walks of life. A great many of these people improved as a result of the healing sessions and many were cured.

The Worralls' method of spiritual healing has been remarkably compatible with the pragmatic techniques used by most scientists. This is probably because Ambrose Worrall was an engineer and, as such, was a stranger neither to science nor the scientific method.

Olga Worrall is just as scientific. She is not the sort of woman given to vague thinking and incoherent conversation. Indeed, five minutes spent talking with her is enough to convince anyone that she is a far cry from the stereotyped mysterious lady of the occult. Mrs. Worrall is a straight-from-the-shoulder person, who believes explicitly in what she and her husband have done.

An interesting part of the Worralls' story, apart from the healing ministry, is that they have never taken a penny in payment for their services.

Since Ambrose Worrall's death in 1972, Mrs. Worrall has carried on as best she can.

There are not as many financial resources as there were when her husband was alive, but she has no wish to slacken the pace she sets for herself, no matter what the obstacles.

A dialogue with Mrs. Worrall is a fascinating, learning experience:

MRS. WORRALL: When we started in 1930 we had a rugged row to hoe. We were unconventional, and the church took a dim view of what we were doing. Somehow or other theologians forgot that the very foundation of Christianity was built on the gifts of the spirit, especially healing.

Healing was practiced by the early church until a certain group of non-spiritual individuals decided that they were the only ones who knew how to interpret God to the laymen. The church and its people have suffered for this.

So all the odds were against us. The church was unsympathetic and the medical profession was rather suspicious.

Average people unacquainted with the various gifts of the Spirit were opposed to our psychic gifts, as well as to spiritual healing, and the more fundamental were certain this was the work of the devil.

When they tell me that, I always say I stand in good company, because that is what they told our Lord when He healed.

We plodded along in our own way. We never took a patient unless he was given proper medical attention or was under the care of a doctor.

What were we supplying?

That extra ingredient that accelerates the normal healing of the physical body. We don't exactly know what spiritual healing is, but it may be akin to electricity. Of course, we don't know exactly what electricity is either. Perhaps someday science will discover the law governing spiritual healing, and then it will be used as an adjunct to medical practice and will enable people to get well much faster.

I would say after forty years of practicing spiritual healing that the church now respects us. It recognizes the fact that we were not out to fleece the public.

Healing results have been obtained, but we did not claim we were the ones who did it.

Only God is able to heal whether He is working

through a medical doctor or a clergyman or a healing channel. Without God's power you are utterly helpless.

Would you agree that the acceptance of your spiritual healing is based on these three factors: (1) you receive no money; (2) you take no personal credit for the success you have achieved; (3) you approach the task of healing with a sense of reverence for the source of your healing energy as part of an as yet unexplained universal law?

MRS. WORRALL: Perhaps. I might also add that we are not challenging these people. We are not a threat to them. But we are a help.

Now, even doctors are more open to the idea of spiritual healing. I have met many, many doctors, and they are, as a rule, very compassionate people.

I find medical people are using spiritual healing; these doctors are praying. The dedicated doctors know they are only channels for this healing energy. They use their skills to mend the body, then that something extra takes over and heals.

Clergymen, too, are now more aware than ever of their responsibility in the field of healing. Ministers are told to teach and preach and heal. They do a lot of preaching, but very little teaching, and absolutely no healing in the average church.

I salute the Episcopalians, because they accepted the idea of the need to provide their people with a healing ministry and have healing services in many of their churches.

I am in the Methodist church. We have been instrumental in keeping the New Life Clinic healing service going because of the healing successes demonstrated. We have people who have started New Life Clinics in their own churches after observing ours.

How did the New Life Clinic get started?

MRS. WORRALL: This was a pioneer project. It was originated in 1950 by Dr. Albert E. Day, Ambrose, and myself. Dr. Day was the one who had nerve enough to want a healing service in his church. He was severely criticized by his colleagues, but the clinic has survived.

Has there been any serious analysis of the case work done by you and your husband?

MRS. WORRALL: I have thousands of letters from people who testify to the healings. I am not in any financial position to have them documented or to have an analysis made.

I am really, frankly, not very interested in proving documentation, because if a person gets well that is all I need to know. That is the important thing.

The miracle healings of Jesus are documented in the Bible. What has the church done with all that documentation? Has it analyzed His healings?

If people want to testify to their healings, they can do so in writing. We do not encourage them to do so publically in our New Life Clinic.

Our healing service is conducted in a very dignified, very quiet way. When the people come to the rail for the laying on of hands, we don't ask them if they have been saved. It is none of our business. We don't ask them what their denomination is. That is none of our business.

Our business is to do the laying on of hands and permit God to use us as a channel, to bring healing into the life of that person.

Would it be fair to say yours is a universalist point of view in that the qualifications of the sufferer are of no interest to you?

MRS. WORRALL: When some ministers ask, "What if nothing happens?", I always tell them that is none of their business. If you are willing to permit God to use you as a channel, whether anything happens or not, then the result is none of your business. Your only business is to permit God to use you.

What are your feelings about the future of spiritual healing?

MRS. WORRALL: I hope and pray it will increase. So much work has been done by people like my husband and myself and others.

I do feel that present-day spiritual healing has made a terrific impression on the layperson.

Perhaps one day the church will wake up to the necessity of a healing service, because if it doesn't the church is going to be empty. If we can fill a church on a Thursday morning (which is an odd day) to overflowing with people who are there crying out for spiritual healing, this should be a sign for the churches to provide this type of ministry for all people. These people attend for soul healing, as well as for physical healing.

What do you mean by soul healing?

MRS. WORRALL: I feel a person is soul-sick when he doesn't have communion with God. His soul is crying out for this communion and very often this soul-sickness will reflect itself in the physical body.

Doctors call this psychosomatic illness. The two are the same thing.

If you can bring peace into a man's mind, assure him that he is God's child, that God is concerned about his well-being, that those who have passed on ahead are very much alive and are eagerly awaiting his coming, that we do live after death, then you can heal and bring peace to the soul. This is thus reflected in the physical body and many illnesses disappear.

Do you believe the mind of man is part of the consciousness of God?

MRS. WORRALL: Yes! It is part of God. You have a mind that functions outside of the body.

When you go to sleep at night you often have astral experiences. There is something in you, something unexplained. You can call it the mind, the God-spark. It is in command at all times. You can describe the physical body; you cannot describe the mind.

Psychiatrists deal in the treatment of mental illness—diseased minds and unhealthy emotions. You are talking about the treatment of soul-sickness. Are they aspects of the same thing?

MRS. WORRALL: Psychiatrists recognize the fact that they have to reach or heal the mind first. They will tell you they have never "healed" a person. They have helped, but they have never really cured a person.

My husband was once approached by a group of psychiatrists who asked him to teach them "instant psychiatry."

That is much of what Jesus did.

I feel that if psychiatrists would pay sensitive attentive attention to the soul of man, the spirit of man, they could perceive the real cause of a person's sickness. They would have instant psychiatry.

When I perceive a person's problem, I don't beat around the bush.

I have absolutely no patience with the idea of blaming other people for what we do. I don't go for that because I was the tenth child in a family of seventeen, and we were not given every privilege. We were given responsibility and chores to do.

Today young people want responsibility.

When I was a schoolteacher, I discovered that the children who came from poor yet disciplined families were, on the whole, very responsible. Some of the others who were pampered and had every whim catered to were just like a ship without a rudder, irresponsible and undisciplined.

How should the gift of spiritual healing be developed?

MRS. WORRALL: I would suggest that every minister, doctor, and psychiatrist be taught to be aware of their gifts of the spirit, and utilize these gifts fully and effectively.

Are you saying that everyone can become a spiritual healer?

MRS. WORRALL: I am not saying that at all. I am saying that anyone who has a desire to go into medicine or nursing is often a natural-born spiritual healer. These persons heal without realizing it. If our doctors were given a course in parapsychology, they would be better able to understand spiritual healing.

I have found very few doctors who are not healers, but many of them can't talk about it because the medical profession is so opposed to unorthodox healing. These dedicated doctors do use their gifts *sub rosa* and many of them have told us they pray before they operate.

There are those, too, who are natural-born diagnosticians who receive this knowledge intuitively. They don't "study" intuition in medical school.

I know many doctors who are truly holy men.

Do many doctors tell you they possess the gift of spiritual healing power?

MRS. WORRALL: They don't tell me. I tell them.

They look at me and smile. God love them! My heart goes out to these dedicated men and women who know the source of their power.

As one recently said to me, "I know I only repair the body. God does the healing."

Is it possible to train spiritual healers?

MRS. WORRALL: No, not unless the person has the potential gift lying dormant. You have it or you don't have it.

But you can refine your gift, and you do learn methods that make it possible to use your gift more effectively.

When you perform the laying on of hands, do you intuitively know what to do?

MRS. WORRALL: Yes. You know where to put the hands.

Certain states do not permit healers to put their hands below the shoulders as protection for unsuspecting people against unscrupulous, so-called healers, and I approve.

However, if the healing is going to be performed in a doctor's office or under supervision, the healer can put his hands on that area of the body.

I have found, though, that this really isn't always necessary; very often a handclasp will heal the person.

Is this a transfer of energy, and does it flow from a healer who is prepared to a patient who may or may not be prepared?

MRS. WORRALL: I feel that it helps if the patient is prepared.

When a person comes to me and says, "Help me," I find this need triggers off that force in me.

I cannot turn my healing on at will. The person may ask me for healing; but if there isn't that immediate attunement, the energy might be released, but would miss its mark. Therefore, we would continue trying until such time when proper attunement would be achieved.

There must be compatibility, then?

MRS. WORRALL: Compatibility is one of the several ingredients in spiritual healing.

Is it possible your gifts may be lost because of a lack of acceptance for spiritual healing?

MRS. WORRALL: Not at all! In spite of all past opposition our gifts have flourished and our gifted young people should be developed.

I made the statement to a group of ministers that if I had my way every church would have a developing circle that would meet once a week under proper supervision to permit our young people to be able to experience psychic phenomena. You make such a suggestion, and some unenlightened soul thinks it is the work of the devil.

Yet God's work will continue regardless of such thinking or opposition.

CHAPTER 23

Huna Healing Techniques

For many years I was fascinated by the healing
methods associated with the Kahunas, the medicine
men and women of the Polyncsian islands.

In February of 1972, my friend Brad Steiger and I
had an opportunity to study certain of the Huna
healing techniques at firsthand when we visited the
Hawaiian islands. Brad later went on to make an
extensive exploration of Huna magic; and for a time he
became professionally associated with Max Freedom
Long, a man who had come to Hawaii in 1917 and who
had become intrigued by the tales of the Kahunas, the
"keepers of the secret" from the very first. Long spent

several years in Hawaii in an attempt to crack the secret code of the Kahunas; and by the time of his death on September 23, 1971, he was considered by many to be the world's greatest authority on the Polynesian psycho-religious system known as Huna.

Brad and I have spent endless hours discussing the ancient methods of the Kahunas in regard to healing and the control of pain. The Kahunas also emphasized special breathing techniques and a system of mental discipline somewhat similar to my own. Because it may add yet another dimension to the concept of self-mastery and the positive applications of mental energies, I am including a discussion of Huna healing in this book.

As a young schoolteacher in Hawaii, Max Freedom Long could at first find no native islander who would speak to him at any length whatsoever about Huna. Long kept at his research like a persistent dog after an elusive hare, for he was undergoing a personal spiritual search, and the native religion seemed to offer yet another avenue of psychic exploration.

At last Max met Dr. William Tufts Brigham, curator of the Bishop Museum, a man heavy with both scientific honors and girth. Dr. Brigham took a liking to the earnest young seeker, and he told him of the time that he had witnessed a Kahuna lava-walk.

"I tried it..."—he grinned at the memory—"and burned off my heavy mountain boots. While I ran for safety with scorched toes, the old Kahunas crossed the lava with their bare feet."

How had they protected their feet?

"They had not treated their feet with anything," Dr. Brigham explained. "They prayed to the Goddess of the Sky for protection from the heat, and it was given. No one even got singed."

The old curator went on to tell the enthralled young schoolteacher how the Kahunas accomplished astounding healings and amazing feats of psychic phenomena.

"What incredible powers do these people possess?" Max wanted to know.

"They have a system of psychology and religion which is pure enough and close enough to its source—whatever that may have been—to work for them," Dr. Brigham said.

"If you want to study it and try to learn the secret behind what they did, remember to watch for three things: some unit of *consciousness* guiding some *unit of force* making it work through some *form of substance*. I know that the secret will be very scientific when you find it, but it has eluded me for forty years!"

Many years later, Max Freedom Long returned to the mainland in defeat.

In his conscious mind he had exhausted every avenue of research. But his unconscious mind had not yet raised the white flag of surrender.

He was awakened one night in 1935 by a bursting light energy which seemed to suffuse the entire room and which shook his intellect with the frenzy of sudden revelation.

He no longer saw through a glass darkly.

It occurred to him with new insight that since the Kahunas had names for the elements in their magic, these words might be found in the Hawaiian-English dictionary that had begun to be formulated as early as 1820. He knew that the Hawaiian language is constructed from short root words and that a translation of the root usually gives the original meaning of a word.

He sat down with his immense volume of personal

notes and began to sort the accumulated research of over forty years' study that had been bequeathed to him by Dr. Brigham.

It was this revelation that enabled Max Freedom Long to crack the ancient code of the Kahunas.

The very essence of Huna lies in the belief that man possesses three souls: the *uhane,* a weak, animal-like spirit that talks; the *unihipili,* a secretive spirit that sticks to, and often hides, another spirit; and the *Aumakua,* the older parental spirit, composed of both male and female elements, that has the low self *(unihipili)* and the middle self *(uhane)* under its guidance.

In psychological terms, one might say that, centuries before Freud, the Kahunas had discovered the conscious *(uhane),* the unconscious *(unihipili),* and the superconscious *(Aumakua).*

"I had found the three elements which Dr. Brigham had stipulated any successful system of magic must employ," Max said. "I determined that Huna works as a system because it contains a *form of consciousness* that directs the magical processes, a *force* utilized by the consciousness that provides the necessary power, and a *substance,* visible or invisible, through which the force can act."

The *Aumakua,* the High Self, is the "god" within each man. It is on this level, above man's waking, conscious level, that one has the power to perform miracles.

According to Huna belief, man's three spirits are surrounded, or encased, in three shadowy bodies composed of a substance called *aka.* Each body of man is fed by its own supply of *mana,* vital force.

The low self *(unihipili)* utilizes simple *mana;* the

middle self *(uhane)* feeds on a more highly charged *mana-mana;* the High Self *(Aumakua)* operates on *mana-loa.*

It is the role of the middle self to instruct the low self to store an extra supply of *mana* to be held in readiness for the time when it is necessary to reach up the connecting *aka* cord and make contact with the High Self.

It is the High Self, the "god" within, that brings about the desired conditions asked in those prayers formed by the combined efforts of the three selves.

"The one rule of life in Huna is that no man should do anything that might hurt another," Max often stated.

"The only sin is to harm another human being."

The more advanced Kahunas added loving service to their fellowman to this rule.

The Kahunas became terribly confused when the missionaries arrived to tell them that all men had sinned against God. They simply did not believe that any man could harm a higher being.

In vain they would protest to the stern, unyielding missionaries: "I cannot sin against God! I am too small."

Max believed that he had found strong evidence that the Egyptians were equally aware of the *aka* threads.

"In some of the drawings in the tombs we see a spider pictured hanging by a thread of web above a mummy case," he explained.

"The spider was the symbol of the *aka,* or shadowy thread, at its best. In the outer teachings, it was said that one had to climb a thread of spider web to get up to heaven.

"The cord that goes between the body and the High Self is made up of many threads, these forming a cord—the silver cord mentioned in the Old Testament.

"In Huma, the web with the spider in the center, with threads reaching out in all directions, was the favorite symbol used to describe the mechanism.

"In Tibet there was once a whole system of belief developed in which the universe was said to be like a web and the souls of men like tiny spiders dotted here and there over the vast web.

"The aborigines in Australia still have a sacred string which is a part of their magic kit.

"In Easter Island, the umbilical cord was the symbol, and such cords were carefully preserved after birth.

"In Polynesia, the word for low self *(unihipili)* had several meanings, one of which was 'sticky.' This refers to the *aka* threads which, like the thread of web exuded by a spider, is at first sticky and will adhere to anything."

Max Freedom Long believed that the "silver cord" of *aka* substance is our means of contact with our High Selves. It is the "telephone line" we use when we call up to ask for help or just to say that we love life.

This "telephone wire" has *mana* as its electricity, *mana* which flows from the low to the High Self, then back again when we use the mystic phone in prayer or worship.

Telepathy, Max Long maintained, is the conversation of two or more people along the telephone wire of *aka* substance. It employs the same mechanism as conversation with the High Self.

And it is most important to realize that *all prayer is telepathic,* and all telepathy is made up of messages sent in picture form by the low self.

Max gave careful advice as to how to best send the proper pictures to the High Self:

If you picture yourself in perfect health and impress that image on the low self as the thing to send as a "want" to your High self, the low self will create a picture of you in perfect health and will send the picture.

The way the High Self answers the prayer is "make real" or "materialize" the picture into reality for you. This is the secret of secrets in Huna.

But get this: the picture of perfect health must *not* be one that includes your sickness.

If you pray, "Heal my illness," the low self will make a picture of you sick and miserable and send it for the prayer. With it will go a picture of you wanting something and perhaps an image of you as well and healthy. The result is a muddle and nothing is given to the High Self to change your condition.

We must *believe* that we are receiving perfect health.

We must *hold the thought* of ourselves well and happy.

If we do not, we inevitably send a sick picture to the High Self to spoil the good picture of perfect health we have already sent up in prayer.

Making the picture of perfect health must be done with the use of the *mana* in order to get a lasting memory of thought-form picture to keep recalling and sending frequently to the High Self.

Make and memorize your picture with breathing in order to collect the *mana* and give the picture enough strength to hold together while the High Self materializes it into actuality for you.

Instruct your low self to send the picture and plenty of *mana* to the High Self, like a telepathic message. The low self knows how, so just set it to work.

Repeat your prayer action at least once a day and continue until the answer is given.

Have faith.

Tell yourself that perfect health is already given on the level of the High Self and is already real.

Live in the picture.

Feel it.

Keep your mind off your ills.

This is the key to real magic. It is yours to use, if you will.

Max often told people that they might have natural healing abilities that could be put to good use helping others to achieve health. He was always challenging his Huna research associates and others to make a test of their abilities to heal.

Cuts, burns, and breaks are good to practice on, Max remarked.

"With daily treatments with *mana,* a surprising response may be brought about. The Kahunas of old could often heal a broken bone in a few minutes. *Mana* hastens the healing process greatly if properly applied."

Max always cautioned the neophyte healer that the first step in administering the curative touch is to breathe deeply, slowly, rhythmically. At the same time, one is to silently ask his low self to manufacture a large *mana* charge.

When the healer feels that he is well "charged up," he is to make a mental picture of himself and his low self causing the patient to be in perfect health. When this is accomplished, he is to picture the call being made to his High Self.

"Don't *talk* the picture, as that just makes words, and the low and High Selves need pictures constructed of *mana*-strengthened thought-forms," Max emphasized.

"Keep your mouth shut and your mind open! The mental picture is your plan, your blueprint, your roadmap . . . the mold which will be used to remold the conditions of illness to perfect health."

Once the healer has the picture firmly in mind, he is to advance to his patient and place his fingers lightly on the place that hurts or that is injured and requires healing.

If, for one reason or another, it is impossible to touch the injured area, the healer should touch the hand or head of the subject, then hold his hands a small distance away from the subject's body on either side of the seat of the trouble.

"The low self can project the *mana* through the shadowy thread the touch establishes if you mentally request it to do so," Max said.

"While holding your hands in position, retain the picture in your mind of the call going to your High Self, then of the *mana* flowing through your fingers and into your patient to charge up the part to be restored."

According to Kahuna methodology, the treatment can last a minute or two, then the healer can pull away, recharge with *mana,* and repeat the treatment as many times as the healer feels is necessary.

The healer should end by giving silent thanks to the High Self and then to the low self, after which he should wash his hands while telling himself that he is washing all the subject's illness or imperfections down the drain, never to return. Such a "down the drain" procedure will keep the healer from possibly picking up his patient's pains through suggestion.

Once when he was asked if the Huna healing method were not, in essence, the very ancient practice of "laying on of hands," Max Freedom Long replied that it most certainly is.

"But in Huna we learn what, besides making a prayer, we are to do in the ancient healing ritual," he explained.

"One does not have to touch the one who is being treated after an *aka* thread of contact has been established. So-called 'absent healing' makes good use of the *aka* threads without knowing that they are doing so. Look at a person, hear his voice or see his picture, and your low self can pick up a thread and follow it in a flash in order to contact the person."

Max Freedom Long believed the central theme of Huna to be prayer and the obtaining of answers to prayer.

He learned that when the Kahunas were still at work in old Hawaii they had a ritual in which the native priest withdrew from the sight of the people gathered before the crude temple platform and entered a grass house reserved for "braiding the cord." Out of sight, perhaps with a chant, he gathered the *aka* threads from the silent worshippers, who were praying for the good of the land, and braided, or united, them into a single strong strand which would reach to the High Selves who were watching.

The Kahuna made a mental picture of the land as it should be and sent this image as the "seed" of the prayer to the High Selves to be made to grow into reality. His prayer was not a brief one.

It was a lengthy ritual done under various taboos. If the prayer was performed correctly, results were expected in due course of time.

In the Huna code, the word for "braid" was *u-la-na*. The first root, *u* is "I, myself," the same as the one used in *u-hane* for the middle self. It tells man that *he* is the one to do the work of praying.

The root *la* is "light," the symbol for the High Self, telling man to whom the prayer is to be sent.

The combined roots *(lana)* mean "to float," which symbolizes the flow of *mana* along the braided cord. The steam of *mana* carries with it the thought forms of the prayer, the "seeds" of the prayer.

In Hawaiian, the word for "worship" is *ho-ana*. *Ho* is from the root "to make." *Ano* is a seed.

In the Huna code we learn that the act of worship is to create a prayer "seed" to send with accumulated *mana* along the *aka* cord to the High Self.

The Hawaiian word for the answer to a prayer is *ano-hou*. Once again we find the root for "seed" and the root *hou*, which has several meanings.

Hou may be translated "to make new or to restore," or "to change a form or appearance."

"*Hou* also means 'to pant or to breathe heavily'," Max said.

Deeper breathing is necessary to the accumulation of the *mana* which is to carry the seed along the *aka* cord to the High Self to make it strong to answer our prayers, to make the seed idea grow into the hard fact.

"The united, or blended, male and female selves, who graduate up from the middle-self level to become a new High Self, are still in a way like the lower selves in the body and are in need of a form of 'sex union' to start the creative act of making the answer for the prayer . . . The lore of India has many statues of the gods in close sexual embrace.

"The true meaning of this divine cohabitation seems

to be that our prayers and gifts of *mana* cause the High Selves to come together in a slightly closer union in order to engage in some form of activity which parallels our sex act in that it is the beginning of their creating something."

Max Freedom Long learned that some groups who studied Huna sought to project *mana* through the hands of the members of a healing circle, and to use their combined "wills" to make the *mana* flow into someone upon whom their hands had been laid.

In addition, they might then recite a prayer of healing, such as the following:

"Father-Mother, we hold this friend of ours to the Light for healing. Give him/her *life*."

Max advised that one might compose a prayer that would suit all the members of a healing circle, but once the group had decided upon such a prayer, it should be recited only by the leader of the circle while all other members remained with their hands on the subject in a quiet and prayerful attitude.

The prayerful quiet should be held for at least half a minute, then the leader of the circle should end the group prayer with the words of the Kahunas of old:

"Our prayer takes flight. Let the rain of blessings fall. *Ah-mana-mana*."

Max admonished:

"The idea is to close the prayer action and not let it hang dangling.

"*Mana* goes where it is directed and does what it is asked to do if one has full confidence so that one's low self believes that what is being done will get results.

"*Mana* will travel or be projected not only by direct

physical contact (which is easiest), but along the line of sight to a person.

"The help that one can give oneself with self-suggestion is also great, but like other ways of projecting or manipulating the *manas* of the body, one must slowly train the low self and get it to understand what part it is to play in the work."

Max Freedom Long's careful analysis of Huna convinced him that if one felt that his life might be improved upon in various ways, the application of a simple technique practiced with determination could bring about the desired changes.

First, Max advised, one must determine precisely what is wanted in one's life, then decide to take steps to obtain it.

Get a small journal or account book that may be carried in pocket or purse.

"Write down all the things that you want to try to do or become with the help of the low self and the High Self. You will practice self-suggestion on the one, and prayer on the other," Max said.

"Go through the list and pick out the things you feel are most important to you and those near and dear to you.

"That done, write out the commands you will use in self-suggestion. For instance: 'I am eating the right amounts of the right food every day.'

"When you have worked out and written several commands to your satisfaction, memorize them. Get the High Self to help by accumulating *mana* and by sending the thought-forms of the prayer-commands to it.

"Get off by yourself. Tense one or two muscles at a time and relax them completely. Recall your commands and use them to order your low self to help: 'I am becoming a better person. I am getting better and better.'

"In the relaxed condition, your low self will accept the suggestions and act on them. *Believe* that you are obeying the commands. That's all there is to it!"

CHAPTER **24**

Eleven Keys to Happiness

As you were able to perceive, the Huna emphasis on special breathing techniques and a system of structured mental discipline presents each of us with yet another perspective on how we might attain self-mastery. As I have stated repeatedly, a proper attitude is so important in accomplishing pain control and healing or self-healing.

The New Age mystic, Francie, wife of author Brad Steiger, also stresses that one must attune himself or herself to the correct vibrations if effective growth and healing are to occur. Herewith Francie offers pertinent advice on achieving an anxiety and pain free life:*

"Healings are accomplished when a person's imbalanced vibratory rate has become normalized or returned to its proper frequency.

"In Biblical accounts, we recall the procedure of casting out evil before the beleagured victim could become healed. This technique was practiced even when the afflicted had carried an infirmity from birth.

"Recently, a group of medical researchers in France performed healings by subjecting their patients to sounds emitted at varying frequencies.

"Numerous journalists have written accounts of men and women having been healed through music.

"Most of us have read the many articles which have appeared dealing with tests which determined the sensitivity of plants to various vibratory influences. It has, for example, been recognized that plants respond favorably to the soothing sounds of symphonic music, but that they withdraw and eventually die when subjected to the harsh sounds of acid rock music. Many tests have been conducted and have proven the growth rate of plants respond positively to the love vibration, and negatively (little growth) to the hate vibration."

*For additional information about Francie's work and her channeled materials, write to *Starbirth,* P.O. Box 4902 Scottsdale, AZ 85258.

ELEVEN KEYS TO HAPPINESS

From time to time we have all experienced the emotion of anxiety, which creates unhappiness.

We worry and fret that a certain event may occur which will jeopardize our happiness.

Many individuals suffer needlessly because they permit this emotion to rule their lives.

An imbalance in one's attitude toward anything brings about the existence of such an emotion, while fear triggers its awakening. When our attitude toward anyone or anything is not balanced, we will experience unhappiness.

Unhappiness can exist only when we are not fully aware.

When we cannot see the total picture, or the reason for the existence of certain events in our lives, we are blind and will experience unhappiness.

We do not realize that it was for these very events, by which to gain knowledge, that our Soul chose to exist in this dimension.

Without these events, what knowledge would be truly gained?

It is through knowledge that our vibrations are raised, as well as those of our Soul.

Eternal happiness results when we raise our vibrations. It would be better if we learn to accept the sorrow in our lives just as we accept joy, for they go hand in hand in that both raise our knowledge and vibrations toward God and the higher realm.

In this physical world of matter, mankind spends the greatest part of its life seeking happiness.

This longing was placed within us for the purpose of

promoting a quest for contentment. This quest causes us to enter into far more experiences than we normally would, and toward paths which provide us with greater knowledge.

I was told by my Parent Guide that we should consider the laws given us in our Bible—the "Thou shalt nots"—as "Keys to Happiness," rather than commandments, for it was for this reason they were given.

They were not meant to be taken as threats, with eternal hellfire as the punishment, but were given with love to provide us with more knowledge by which we might attain not only happiness but the raising of our vibrations to the Hierarchal realm. The main sin is interfering with the progression of another to the higher realm, which ceases our own elevation.

I was given the knowledge that one should add this phrase to the end of every commandment—"And you will find happiness!"—and we will better understand each commandment's meaning.

The "First Commandment" or "Key to Happiness" given us was, "Place no other God before me." Add— "And you will find happiness!"

It was known that we possess a great need for love, for it is of the highest vibration.

When we place too great a love, surpassing all other love, on anything of this world, we jeopardize our own happiness.

We know that all matter is perishable, be it a person, animal, or object—all can be destroyed. God, being not of the material world, is imperishable.

Therefore, the first Key to Happiness is not placing another love so as to create a God above the love we feel for Him. In this way, our greatest feeling of love is made more secure.

Let us consider another commandment: "Keep holy the sabbath day." Add—"And you will find happiness!"

In setting aside one day of the week to think of God, we will achieve a more balanced perspective, withdraw our interest from the material world, and place it in the spiritual world. In this way we will achieve a greater balance in our attitude, and thereby become more content. Also, in doing this, we will be more able to love God above all things of earth.

Of the commandment to "Honor thy father and thy mother," add—"And you will find happiness!"

Psychiatrists have long since recognized that the two people we first come in contact with, and our feelings toward them, govern our attitude toward all others that follow. Thus, by honoring our parents, we achieve greater happiness throughout our lives in our relationship with others.

Now, with this "Key," open your understanding of all other commandments given.

Thou shalt not kill, *and you will find happiness.*

The reasoning is obvious, as are all truths. When we destroy a facet of life-form occupied by the Soul, we destroy the achievement of further knowledge. In doing this, we thwart the raising of the vibrations of all involved—the one destroyed, his soul's, our own, and those of our soul.

Think then of the Key to Happiness or commandment—"Thou shalt not covet thy neighbor's goods . . . and you will be happy."

If we desire that which belongs to another, will we be happy?

And of the Key to Happiness, "Thou shalt not covet thy neighbor's wife," add—"and we will find happiness." Think of the unhappiness that would result if all people stole from one another.

The Master-Teacher Jesus gave us an Eleventh Key to Happiness when he told us to "Love One Another." If this were followed and this Key used, would it not open the doors of happiness to all?

With these Keys we will become as one with our Soul and join the Hierarchy.

RECEIVING COMFORT WHILE GROWING FROM TRIALS AND TRIBULATIONS

There is an ancient Chinese proverb which states that a gem cannot be polished without friction, nor can a man be perfected without trials.

From our limited perspective, the trials and tribulations which afflict us seem in themselves to be evil. It is hard to perceive that such situations are actually opportunities for growth and are good for us.

I once had a dream-vision in which I saw a woman suffering many hardships. While she struggled in her tears, I saw an Angel from the Heavenly Realm smiling.

The Angel was not being sadistic or delighting in the woman's sorrow, but knew that the woman was growing and gaining strength because of her suffering on the Earth plane. It is as if a tear in this dimension is equal to a smile in the Higher Vibration.

Or, as H. W. Beecher once remarked, "Tears are often the telescope by which men see far into heaven."

We must experience many ordeals to gain the higher vibrations of knowledge and awareness. Those experiences that provide the greatest gain often take the form of sorrows and tribulations.

Men and women have come to me often with eyes that are red from constant tears. "Why me?" they so often ask. "Why am I going through this terrible time? The lessons are too severe!"

But whoever learns strength from unceasing joy? And, regretfully, how many men and women even give pause to think of the deeper truths when everything is going well for them?

I am always troubled when I hear certain sincere men and women complaining that Satan has beset them with adversities.

"That evil demon has brought this sorrow to me," they insist. "Why does this evil thing happen to me?"

I have been told that we must never overlook the loving hand and heart of the Hierarchy in our trials on the Earth plane, as all events are "Soul Chosen" for our Learning.

If we perceive our tribulations as acts of evil directed against us, then we have made them rigidly absolute and powerful evils which cannot possibly be eased by any remedy or relief.

If we persist in viewing our afflictions apart from God and the Hierarchy, we cannot be comforted—nor can we find any meaning to our troubles.

It is best to meet affliction head-on, so that we might pass through it solemnly, slowly, and with humility and faith.

Perhaps we might even sit down and evaluate past tribulations and assess what we have learned from those ordeals which we have already survived.

We might even make up a list of the good things

which evolved from an act which, at the time, we considered intensely evil. In this way we prepare ourselves for future ordeals that may come.

Sometimes when one is severely depressed and weighted down with the problems of his distressful situation, he concludes that he has been judged and found to be bad and deserving of punishment. Just as we should not think of our trials as acts of evil, neither should we deem them to be Divine sentences of punishment.

Consider these things:

We could never experience true joy unless we had tasted of deep sorrow.

We could never know contentment if we had not undergone adversity.

We could never truly know charity if we had not been wrongly accused.

We could never really practice generosity if we had never been poor.

We could never exercise the grace of forgiveness if we had not been dealt with severely by our enemies.

Perhaps we might visualize the Earth plane as a great metal-working shop in which we are continually being heated in the forge and hammered on the anvil.

If we can permit the analogy that we are pliant metal being worked by the steady strokes of the Hierarchy's hammer of experience, then we can understand how those skillful, albeit painful, blows are shaping us for higher, more noble, things.

The virtuous person may be compared to good metal. The more he is fired, the more he is refined.

The more powerfully he is hammered, the more he is magnificently shaped.

The blows may try him and stun him, but he will never emerge from the anvil misshapen. He will always bear the fine stamp of quality workmanship.

It is so easy to obey the commandments of God and the teachings of the Heirarchy when we are led along pleasant pathways. It requires no effort to trust in the Heavenly Host when the path is brightly illuminated in golden sunshine. Our greatest moral victories come when we walk resolutely along the pathway when it is shrouded in darkness and the way is confused with the angry flashing of terrible lightning overhead.

We know of the promises and the ever-present succor of the Hierarchy.

We have learned of their Great Plan.

Once we have been made aware of the total picture, the complete plan of spiritual evolution, how can we be reluctant to permit ourselves to be weighed in the golden scales of God?

CHAPTER 25

You Are Gods in the Making

I am a normal, emotional human being.

I have had no training whatsoever in the esoteric realm. I have been my own teacher.

I was able to build my own reality, and you, too, have that same potential.

I have been in many scientific laboratories being checked out by neurosurgeons, psychiatrists, psychologists, and anthropologists to determine whether I am, indeed, a "normal" man.

In the neurological workup done by C. Norman Shealy, Director of the Pain Rehabilitation Center in La Crosse, Wisconsin, it was revealed that when I was in my "normal" state, I was super-sensitive, not only to pain, but to the sensation of touch itself. When I was asked to regulate the flow of blood, the temperature of my body, and the performance of autonomous physical functions, the sophisticated electronic machinery indicated that I dropped into a deep alpha-brainwave state.

The puzzled doctors asked me how I could raise and lower body temperatures and control pain, but I had to answer simply that I just made it happen.

I did not learn pain control by reading, studying, or by contemplation. I spent the majority of my life working to attain this mastery over pain.

In other laboratory tests, I have been able to heal open, bleeding wounds within fifteen minutes to the extent where there was no physical mark remaining to indicate that a cut had ever been made.

I was taken to the physics department at Kent State University where work had been done with the remarkable Uri Geller and the respected healer Olga Worrall. Here Dr. Wilbur Franklin asked me to distinguish metal balls from marbles in sealed containers, to identify the colors of covered playing cards, and to cause the deviation of a laser beam by mind power.

Although I was able to accomplish these challenges in a satisfactory manner, I will be the first to admit that such tasks are only tests, with little practical value.

In my opinion, it takes the spiritual essence of man to activate the physical and the mental aspects of his makeup. Once the total mechanism has been activated, each man and each woman should be able to derive a full, pragmatic utilization of these abilities.

As a result of the probings of many doctors at several scientific laboratories, it would appear that I have had such abilities since the age of three. I enhanced these natural abilities through an application of the yogic techniques of proper breathing.

It is unnecessary to spend your lives running from teacher to teacher, from guru to guru, when you have the knowledge of self-mastery already within you. All you need is something to prompt the knowledge from you.

I will hope that you will be able to find such a catalyst in this book. I discovered my own catalyst in my involvement in mankind.

I am definitely against one withdrawing from life to enter a life of seclusion and esoteric study. One can find all the secrets for which he seeks in everyday life and be considered a normal individual.

It does not matter what meditation technique one uses, what brainwave pattern he affects, what plateau of spirituality he has achieved, if he is able to accomplish things which benefit him in a practical way.

If you are ready to get on the way, you must make a commitment. You may have to change your whole life-style.

I live a very serene life, because I am not bothered by the trivia of the world which seems to affect and to bother so many men and women.

I have released my concern for the acquisition of material things.

By devoting my time to practicing the six steps to self-mastery, I have eliminated the need for the extraneous details of living.

To reiterate the six steps, first, there is "Ego."

Immediately, some always retreat when I mention the term. They believe that it is not spiritual to emphasize ego.

But what I am talking about is the magic of

believing in yourself. If you don't believe strongly enough in yourself, you will never advance. You will stay, "plop," on the ground.

Neither, of course, should one develop egotism, because that will, indeed, keep you on the ground.

And just because you *think* positive is no sign that your attitude *is* positive.

A positive attitude is extremely important in achieving self-mastery. One must make a total commitment to maintaining an ever-positive attitude.

By the same token, it is through the negativity around you that you are able to learn and to grow. Therefore, one should not become obsessed with removing all negativity from his immediate environment. A little negativity will only make life more interesting.

When I talk about relaxation, I am talking about good, physical, bodily exercise. If you tone only the mind, you are placing limitations upon yourself. Vigorous exercise that gets the blood circulating right to the fingertips, and provides stimulation to the body, is necessary.

The body must be maintained so that it can properly deal with the stresses and strifes of daily living.

If good breathing techniques did nothing more for you than enable you to live, that would be valuable in itself.

But as I have emphasized, complete breathing is essential not only to good health, but to self-mastery.

If you are able to do complete breathing—that is, totally filling the lungs—and then go to rhythmic breathing automatically, you are well into the next step toward self-mastery, because you have gained a focal point through breath control.

The next step is, of course, concentration.

Concentration, in its truest, unadulterated form, means being able to focus the mind on one single, solitary thing. You must be able to focus the mind on a single object and become oblivious to everything else in the world. Nothing else can exist but this one solitary object. Unless you learn to accomplish this mental feat, you cannot learn to meditate correctly.

In the truest form of meditation—the unadulterated form—you are able to bring your mind to complete focus on a single object to the exclusion of everything else, and you are then able to drop that focal point from your mind.

People usually respond to this statement by saying, "Oh, we are then to think of nothing."

If you believe this to be meditation, then you are still very far from the truth.

When I tell you to remove that focused thought from your mind, you now tune in to your subconscious, your superconscious, to the whole universe. You become one with everybody—God, if you wish to call it that. Once you have achieved this point, you can go beyond.

But let us go back to the point where the average John or Jane Doe who thinks he or she meditates really exists—and really is.

Somewhere between concentration and the beginning, fringe areas of meditation, there is a hole into which most men and women fall.

This particular area is ecstasy, the area where you start to hear voices, you start to see things, you start to hallucinate.

This is the area which is utilized by hypnosis, by psychism.

This is not the area where you want to be. In true meditation, you wish to go beyond this point.

In true meditation, you have the possibility of

moving even further into the cosmos and achieving a power so great, so magnificent, that your entire body and mind may become transformed into a more sensitive, more fully functioning entity.

But proper preparation for this state of consciousness is imperative, for the extreme sensitivity may be channeled in other areas, such as intense, nearly uncontrollable, sexual desire. This is an expression to release the energies which are building up within the system. People who are unprepared to cope with such energies may find themselves caught up in an improper release which will subvert them from true self-mastery.

Now is the time to call upon your spiritual guidance so that you will be able to learn true knowledge and to gain pure wisdom. I believe that one actually has ethereal guides and teachers upon whom he might draw. I do not think it is necessary to have such a belief for full expression of self-mastery, but I do believe that it is necessary for each aspirant to self-mastery to become as a child again.

Not childish, I will emphasize, but child-like.

You must have the imagination of a child. You must enter into the realm of a child.

In a child's eyes, nothing is impossible.

You, too, can overcome the impossible.

You can create the reality for which you were truly intended.

You can live in a world that has become justified to your means.

There is something more than man. And it is within man.

When we think of ourselves as human beings, we place limitations upon ourselves. But when we think of ourselves as gods, then nothing is impossible.

You are all gods in the making. Exercise your right to be one.

APPENDIX

*Concerning an Examination of
Komar in Victoria, B.C.,
by David Walker, Northern Lights College*

In April of 1977, we were invited to neuropsychologically test Vernon Craig, an Ohio cheesemaker who, as Komar the Hindu Fakir, holds Guinness world records for: lying longest on a bed of nails (25 hours 20 minutes); supporting the most weight while sandwiched between two beds of nails (1,642 lbs.); and walking the greatest distance (25 ft.) through the hottest (1,494°F) pit of coals.

In the following report we describe our experiences with Komar, including:

Some preliminary considerations based on the work of others.

The rationale and results for the particular neuropsychological tests used.

And a theoretical explanation of the findings.

Previous work by Dr. C. Norman Shealy at the Pain Rehabilitation Center in Lacrosse, Wisconsin, established that Komar's feats could not be explained on the basis of a congenital analgesia or any neurological abnormality (Shealy, 1973).

Furthermore, an investigation by Pelletier and Pepper (1977) of three adepts who performed feats similar to, but lesser than those of Komar, did not reveal any particular physiological response pattern which contributed to an explanation of the phenomenon of absence of pain and serious injury in "normally" traumatic situations.

We reasoned that Komar's feats might result from "gating off" peripheral input at some relatively low CNS (central nervous system) level; or from manipulating some higher level of "CNS," thus rendering himself unresponsive to the input.

To examine these alternatives we used Weinstein filaments to measure the sensitivity of his back to touch, and a dichotic listening test to measure cerebral organization, and information processing. These tests are briefly described below.

The Weinstein filaments are plastic fibres two inches long... These fibres, mounted on a rigid structure, are advanced to the skin surface by an experienced examiner. The subject responds when he feels the touch of a fibre on his skin.

The dichotic listening tests involved the simultaneous presentation of different words to the right and left ears. In the test used, three dichotic pairs separated by X seconds were presented... until a total of 51 pairs had been presented.

APPENDIX 167

Prior to lying on the bed of nails, Komar, seated in a chair, was given the full dichotic listening test and the tactile sensitivity of a skin patch on the left shoulder was determined, using an ascending and descending series of presentation of the Weinstein filaments.

Komar then lay with his shoulders, buttocks, and thighs, supported only by a 2′ × 4′ bed of 4″ nails on 1.5″ centers, while the dichotic listening and tactile sensitivity tests were repeated.

Results

The tactile sensitivity tests revealed that Komar's sensitivity, which was normal in the control condition, was greatly increased while lying on the nails.

In the normal condition Komar detected the fourth smallest stylus in both the ascending and descending series.

In the nail-bed condition Komar detected the second smallest stylus in both ascending and descending conditions.

In the dichotic listening task under normal conditions, Komar successfully identified 27 words presented to the right ear and 13 words presented to the left ear.

Five minutes later, when tested under the nail-bed condition, Komar again showed a right ear superiority, but this time correctly identified 31 words presented to the right ear and 19 words presented to the left ear.

Discussion

The present data are adequate to reject both hypotheses. That Komar's feats are not attributed to some "off gating" mechanism in the low CNS is clearly illustrated by the tactile sensitivity data, while the dichotic listening data shows that his ability is not related to his entering into an unresponsive or "clouded" state.

Neither of the clinical test instruments used in this experiment are supplied with normative test-retest data, which makes it impossible to assess the significance of the improvement in both tests under the nail-bed condition. This outcome is, however, most interesting, and confronted by it, we will discuss it in the interest of stimulating future work.

Pain

According to one neuropsychological theory, pain is the experiential correlate of cerebral disorganization (Hebb, 1949).

This is an attractive hypothesis since the likelihood of survival would be increased in animals if the mediating processes (Hebb, 1949 and 1977) that resulted in the animal receiving a traumatic wound were disrupted and disorganized by the trauma. The hypothesis has received direct support from electrophysiological studies of the response to painful stimuli.

Further support for the hypothesis comes from situations where pain was not experienced although it might have been expected. Such instances include: athletes participating in sporting events ("Budd Played with a Broken Leg," *Vancouver Province,* October 14, 1977); persons using autogenic training for pain relief (Shealy, 1977); and adepts voluntarily submitting themselves to trauma (Pelletier and Pepper, 1977).

In all cases, the "cerebral organization" of the injured person is unbroken because of a focus upon some consciousness-capturing activity.

If cerebral disorganization is the necessary and sufficient cause of pain, and maintaining or heightening cerebral organization is necessary to eliminate pain, then one might conjecture that during the nail-bed test Komar must have been in a highly organized state.

Direct observation of Komar supports this conjecture, because in our studies he was, in effect, directing our procedures; in other situations, he carefully directs the placement of up to 1,642 pounds of jiggling bodies that sandwich him between the nail beds.

The results of our neuropsychological tests also support the hypothesis that Komar was in a state of heightened cerebral organization during the nail-bed tests.

While the importance of this dimension of brain activity is just becoming apparent, Hebb's theory of cerebral organization predicts that very weak inputs would stand a better chance of becoming suprathreshold in an organized and "attending cortex" than in a disorganized cortex.

The interpretation of the neuropsychological findings from Komar, supports Hebb's (1949) theory of cerebral organization and the assertion that cerebral disorganization is experienced as "pain." From the practical standpoint they also reinforce the emerging picture from autogenic therapy (Shealy, 1977) and the study of adepts by Pelletier and Pepper (1977) that a present-centered focus, which eliminates morbid futuristic fears of trauma, is the best means to eliminate pain.

Such a statement is also in agreement with Komar's own comments on his abilities, and with the Buddha's words on Sangsara and suffering.